"You disapprove of me don't you?" he asked

Kate felt suddenly reckless. For once, Nicholas Blake was going to hear the truth about himself. "Yes. I do. You're cold and calculating and you use people for your own advantage."

"So. I'm a businessman, not a plaster saint. My rivals know what to expect." He got to his feet and paced restlessly. "But it's the women you're talking about, isn't it?"

"Yes," she said, defiantly. "I don't approve of playboys."

"Jealous, Kate?" he asked, obviously amused. "Are you piqued because I haven't tried to add you to my conquests? That can be easily remedied."

Even as she began to struggle, Kate knew it was hopeless. No way could she check the shivers of delight that ran through her as his mouth descended on hers....

WELCOME TO THE WONDERFUL WORLD OF *Harlequin Romances*

Interesting, informative and entertaining, each Harlequin Romance portrays an appealing and original love story. With a varied array of settings, we may lure you on an African safari, to a quaint Welsh village, or an exotic Riviera location—anywhere and everywhere that adventurous men and women fall in love.

As publishers of Harlequin Romances, we're extremely proud of our books. Since 1949, Harlequin Enterprises has built its publishing reputation on the solid base of quality and originality. Our stories are the most popular paperback romances sold in North America; every month, six new titles are released and sold at nearly every book-selling store in Canada and the United States.

A free catalogue listing all available Harlequin Romances can be yours by writing to the

HARLEQUIN READER SERVICE,
(In the U.S.) M.P.O. Box 707, Niagara Falls, N.Y. 14302
(In Canada) Stratford, Ontario, Canada N5A 6W2

We sincerely hope you enjoy reading this Harlequin Romance.

Yours truly,

THE PUBLISHERS
Harlequin Romances

Dark Encounter

by

SUZANNA FIRTH

Harlequin Books

TORONTO • LONDON • NEW YORK • AMSTERDAM
SYDNEY • HAMBURG • PARIS • STOCKHOLM

Original hardcover edition published in 1979
by Mills & Boon Limited

ISBN 0-373-02307-3

Harlequin edition published January 1980

Printed in U.S.A.

CHAPTER ONE

'I REALLY don't think there's anything else I can tell you about the job, Helen.' Kate gave the girl by her side what she hoped was an encouraging smile. 'But you've probably got lots of questions to ask?'

'Not about the office layout or the work, Miss Sherwood. You've really explained it all very thoroughly, thanks. What I would like to know more about is——'

'Yes?' Kate prompted as the other girl hesitated.

'Mr Edwards. What's he like? Did you find him easy to work for?'

Kate tried desperately to find a non-committal answer. What would Helen, fresh from secretarial college and overwhelmed at her luck in landing such a good job, think, if Kate told her, 'Mr Edwards is fine to work for, but don't make a fool of yourself by falling in love with him the way I did.'

'Mr Edwards is a very considerate employer,' she said stiffly at last. 'I don't think you'll find you have any problems in dealing with him.'

'I saw the pictures of his wedding in one of the newspapers,' Helen ventured. 'He's very good-looking. I bet he's broken a few hearts in his time.'

Including mine, Kate thought bitterly. She ignored the comment. She no doubt seemed unfriendly by her refusal to discuss the matter, but she was past caring what people thought of her at the moment. Time enough for Jeremy's new secretary to get to know him when his present secretary had left the scene.

After she had shown Helen to the door Kate wandered back to her desk and began to clear the drawers of her personal belongings. Would a sensible person be acting the way she was behaving now, throwing up a good job and running off in an attempt to hide her bruised feelings? But Kate had had her fill of being sensible. 'Little Miss Prudence' Jeremy had nicknamed her, when she had queried some of his riskier business ventures. Jeremy, who had nevertheless coupled with his recklessness a financial acumen which had carried him safely through many a sticky situation. Jeremy, the man she had hoped to marry.

Kate had worked as personal secretary to Jeremy Edwards for two years. With him she had shared the setbacks as well as the triumphs as, with ruthless determination, he had guided his inheritance, the family engineering firm, from near bankruptcy to the profitable position it now occupied. Looking back, Kate realised that it had been quite inevitable that she should love him. His blond good looks combined with his will to succeed and his personal charm of manner to attract every woman he encountered. Yet, incredibly, he had chosen Kate.

It had begun one evening, when, as a reward for the hours of overtime Kate had worked to retype an urgent contract, Jeremy had taken her out to dinner. It was a pleasant meal, for, although Jeremy spent most of it outlining his plans for boosting foreign exports, it seemed that for the first time he was noticing her as a person rather than as an efficient machine which ran his office smoothly, fended off awkward telephone calls and supplied him with endless cups of black coffee.

'You're sweet to bother with all my problems, Kate,' he told her with a smile. 'You spend all the hours of the day looking after me and my affairs and now you've let me bore you all evening with my plans for the business.

Why didn't you tell me to shut up?'

Kate laughed. 'I'm not most girls,' she said calmly. 'I don't find it boring to listen to your ideas for the development of the firm. Besides, I couldn't stay detached from my work, I enjoy it too much.'

'Your friends must think you've got a real slave-driver for a boss, the way you nearly live at the office. I'll make it my New Year's resolution not to work you so hard.'

Kate laughed at the idea of him managing without her efforts. She knew that her flat-mate, Jane, thought she was mad to stay late at the office practically every night. Jane was a strict nine-to-five girl, leaving her office every day with a sigh of relief and rejoicing in a hectic social life which took her out most evenings and week-ends. Although she was aware of Kate's devotion to Jeremy, Jane made it clear that she considered it a waste of time.

'You ought to be out enjoying yourself, not slaving over a typewriter for a man who barely notices you,' she told Kate firmly. 'Show him there are more important things in life than the interests of Edwards Engineering. Can't you see that he just takes you for granted? He's using you, playing on your loyalty to him and the firm to squeeze more work out of you. I'll bet he never pays you overtime for all the extra work you put in on his behalf.'

'Jeremy's not like that,' Kate defended him angrily. 'You don't know him.'

'I've met his type a thousand times before,' Jane said. 'You've not a hope in heaven of attracting his attention, so why not give up now before you get hurt?'

But, sound though the advice might have been, Kate ignored it. What had started out as merely a pleasant working relationship had become more important to her and now filled her life completely. She was the only person to whom Jeremy confided his hopes and fears for the future. Was she wrong to hope that some day he might see her as something more than just his ever reliable secretary?

As the months passed it seemed that Kate's patience was rewarded. Jeremy took her out regularly, often to the theatre, occasionally to a concert or to the ballet. At week-ends, office crises permitting, they drove out of London in Jeremy's car, exploring country villages and eating at quiet inns away from the bustle and noise of the city. She knew that Jeremy enjoyed the time they spent together. 'You're so relaxing, Kate,' he said happily once. 'The one person in the world that I can always rely on completely to look after me. I don't know where I'd be without you.'

Yet, when he finally asked her to marry him, Kate was taken completely by surprise. They had worked late at the office and, as usual, he had driven her home. As the car had drawn up outside the block of flats where Kate lived she had turned to thank him. It had been a shock—albeit a pleasant one—when Jeremy had taken her in his arms and kissed her passionately. 'It won't always be nothing but work in our lives, Kate,' he vowed to her. 'Some day there'll be time for other things, time for us to enjoy ourselves. Will you take a chance on marrying me?'

Not the most romantic of proposals of marriage, Kate thought to herself when later, much later, Jeremy had driven away and she let herself into the flat. As usual Jane was out with one of her many friends and Kate sat alone marvelling at the knowledge that Jeremy loved her and wanted to marry her.

When she returned Jane was stunned by the news and refused to believe it at first. 'Goodness, he's going to some lengths to keep a good secretary!' was her amazed reaction. Then, seeing Kate's crestfallen face, she had made a joke of her surprise and offered her congratulations. 'I hope you'll be very happy. When's the engagement party, then?'

Kate explained that nothing was to be said for the moment. Jeremy was about to embark on negotiations for a merger with another firm and his time for the next weeks would be completely taken up with it. They were postponing the news until there was time for a breathing space. Then they would choose a ring together.

'Well, if anyone's fitted to be a businessman's wife, it's you,' Jane commented. 'I can't think of anyone else I know that would happily postpone announcing their engagement because of a business deal. I hope Jeremy realises what a treasure he's getting.'

The next few weeks were a nightmare of activity for everyone at Edwards Engineering. The proposed merger with a big electrical group, Markham International, occupied all Jeremy's time. Business advisers and accountants took up more and more of his office hours and Kate saw him only briefly as he rattled off answers to vital correspondence and disappeared into the boardroom again almost immediately. Those who were well up in office gossip lost no opportunity of letting her know that the negotiations that Jeremy was conducting involved not only Sir Geoffrey Markham, but also his beautiful daughter Felicity. Kate ignored the rumours and believed Jeremy when he made excuses for not seeing her outside the office.

'Another cocktail party with the Markhams,' he would explain to her cheerfully. 'I don't want to go, darling. You know I'd rather be with you. I'm sorry that it's so vital for me to meet all these business associates of Sir Geoffrey, but you of all people should understand how important it is for me to keep old man Markham happy at this stage in the deal.'

Had it also been important for the merger, Kate wondered, to marry 'old man' Markham's daughter in a brief register office ceremony only a month after Jeremy had promised all his love for her? Kate winced at the recollection. He had not even attempted to explain or apologise. He had merely left her a briefly worded note, indicating that he and Felicity would be away on their honeymoon and that he would be returning to the office in a fortnight's time. It had been impersonal, an office communication between a boss and his very efficient secretary with no indication of what they had ever meant to each other.

Kate reeled under the shock, but somehow carried on with her work that morning. Jeremy was returning in a fortnight, but she certainly didn't intend to be waiting for him, smiling her forgiveness, when he arrived. A week's notice was all that her contract required and she handed in her resignation to one of Jeremy's co-directors the same afternoon.

Surprisingly, beyond asking if she would be willing to interview and select a suitable replacement for herself, he raised no objections or tried to make her change her mind. Perhaps, Kate surmised, he realised that she had been in love with Jeremy. It was a classic case, she supposed, that of the young secretary falling for her attractive employer. What nobody had known was that Jeremy had professed to return that love. 'Pressure of work' had prevented him from buying her a ring. 'I'm frantically busy now the deal's completed. We'll choose a ring together when the pressure's off,' he told her, and she had been happy to wait, what a naïve fool she had been! Business expediency would always come before all else with Jeremy and she did not doubt that whatever Felicity Markham's attractions, her greatest asset for Jeremy was her father's electrical company.

Perhaps she should have stayed on at the office, Kate

wondered, as she stowed her belongings in her bag, took a last glance round the office to check that she had left nothing behind and set off for her flat. Perhaps instead of leaving she should have confronted Jeremy on his return. And said—what? What was done couldn't be undone and Kate was not the sort of girl to try to break up a marriage, even if the opportunity came her way. As she told Jane, admitting defeat, 'I'd have no chance against the beautiful Felicity.'

'Well, they say gentlemen prefer blondes,' her friend replied, glancing at the newspaper photographs of the happy couple. 'She looks a bit like a china doll with that round, pale face and those baby curls. Brought out the protective instinct in him, I suppose. He can look after her and her father's firm at the same time.' She saw the look of misery on Kate's face and tossed the paper aside, making an effort to distract her. 'What are you going to do, Kate? Jobs don't grow on trees nowadays, you know, and it may be a while before you find something else.'

'I know frenzied activity is the usual recommendation when you're unlucky in love,' Kate answered in an attempt to sound flippant, 'but I've had enough of office life at the moment. Even the thought of trudging round looking for another job depresses me.'

'Take a holiday,' Jane suggested. 'You never did get away in the summer when you meant to have a break. Your precious Jeremy wouldn't let you go, if you remember?'

Kate sprang automatically to his defence. 'We were frantically busy in July and Jeremy thought it would be better if I postponed my holiday——'

'And like a fool you agreed with him!' Jane said tartly. 'There's nothing to stop you having a holiday now. A break to get away from it all, although,' she peered dismally out at the rain trickling down the windows of the flat, 'November's not really the month for a holiday, is it? You could go abroad, I suppose, if you liked? Somewhere warm and sunny would be nice at this time of year, even if you are on your own. It's a pity I can't wangle any more holiday out of my boss or I'd offer to join you.'

'I think I'd be pretty poor company at the moment, Jane, but thanks all the same.' Kate pondered the problem. 'I'd prefer to stay in England. For one thing I don't know how long my savings will have to last me before I find another job, and trips abroad are expensive just at the moment.'

'You could always go home. Your parents are always glad to see you,' said Jane. 'You were saying not long ago that they complained that they hardly saw anything of you these days.'

'Yes, I could go home. But I'd be faced with all sorts of questions about why I left Edwards Engineering. They'd understand, of course, but they'd sympathise and try to comfort me, and I couldn't face going over it all again, Jane. I want to go somewhere where I can sort myself out and try to get over it all. Where nobody knows about what happened and——' Kate broke off as a sudden thought struck her. 'Of course—Aunt Meg! I should have thought of her before.'

'You've never mentioned your aunt to me. Where does she live?' Jane asked.

'She's not really my aunt, just an old friend of my mother. She and her husband were neighbours of ours at one time. They were always dreaming about a cottage in the country. They managed to buy a place in one of those tiny Cotswold villages that all the tourists flock to in the summer. In fact, they retired there. Uncle Walter died not long after the move and I think Aunt Meg's found it a bit too quiet for her. In the summer she takes in visitors, as much for the company as the money they bring in, I imagine, but I gather it's very different in the winter months with no one new to talk to for weeks on end sometimes. At least that's the picture we get from the letters she sends to my mother. I haven't had time to go down there and see her, although she's always said I'd be very welcome any time I cared to go and stay.'

'But, Kate, what on earth will you find to do in a Cotswold village in the middle of winter?' Jane protested.

'The break will do me good. Lots of fresh air and exercise is probably exactly what I need at the moment. I'll write to Aunt Meg tonight.'

'Fresh air and exercise! You'll be dead from boredom within a week!'

And Aunt Meg, although pleased at the prospect of seeing Kate for an extended stay, made it clear that she felt much the same way. 'Life here in Westford may seem rather quiet after the bright lights,' her letter ran. 'We have to make our own amusements out here in what you would probably regard as the back of beyond. However, I shall be delighted to see you again.'

She expressed no surprise at Kate's sudden desire to take a holiday in the country in the middle of November and merely enclosed directions for reaching the village. Kate waved the letter at her friend, feeling almost cheerful for the first time since the news of Jeremy's defection.

'Everything settled?'

'Yes. I can stay with Aunt Meg for as long as I like. She says she'll be glad of the company. Business really tails off in the autumn and is non-existent in the winter. Apparently it's the time when she recharges her batteries ready for next year's onslaught, or so she says.'

Jane was still dubious as she sat on the end of Kate's bed that evening and watched her friend pack for her holiday. Even at the last minute she was ready to talk Kate out of the idea.

'It's no use talking any more about it, Jane,' Kate said firmly. 'My mind's made up.'

'Hibernating in the country isn't my idea of fun. Still, if it makes you any happier and gets Jeremy Edwards out of your system, I suppose I ought to be all for it.' Jane grinned at Kate. 'You never know your luck. You might meet some absolutely marvellous man in the middle of nowhere and fall madly in love with him. They say the surest way to forget one man is to fall for another.'

Kate closed the lid of her suitcase with a bang and snapped the locks shut. 'There's no danger of that happening. I may be a fool, but I'm not stupid enough to make the same mistake twice.' She laughed bitterly. 'Thanks to Jeremy I've learnt my lesson. In future I'm steering clear of men, marvellous or otherwise.'

Despite the grey skies and chill in the air Kate felt almost lighthearted as she set off next day for Westford. The battered Mini she drove had both amused and irritated Jeremy, who was always telling her to trade it in for something better.

'It's perfectly all right,' she told him laughingly. 'Stop worrying. It gets me from A to B, which is all that's necessary. I've no claim to be stylish.'

'When we're married,' Jeremy threatened, 'it's going on the scrap heap and you'll get something classier or I'll know the reason why. Can't have the boss's wife driving around in a load of rubbish like this. It's practically an antique.'

There wouldn't be any more arguments about that, Kate thought, as a heavy drive of sleet across the windscreen recalled her wandering attention to the task in hand. Since lunchtime, when she had stopped the car outside Abingdon to eat a few sandwiches and pour herself a cup of coffee from the flask she had brought with her, she had noticed gathering storm clouds ahead of her and had passed on hurriedly, regretting her decision to avoid major roads and take her time over the journey, while enjoying the countryside. She should have realised that the lanes which attracted so many tourists in the summer months presented a very bleak picture at this time of year.

To add to Kate's troubles the windscreen wipers, after battling valiantly against the downpour, finally gave up the ghost. Cursing, she got out of the car to investigate, but the flurries of hail which stung her eyes and numbed her hands frustrated her efforts. She was unmechanical at the best of times, but finding the fault in this weather seemed even more of an impossibility than usual. She gave a last ineffectual poke at the windscreen, but the wipers remained stubbornly jammed. She gave up and got back in the car. The smart brown trouser-suit, which she had thought so suitable for the journey, was soaked and her shoes squelched dismally. She shivered and wished that she'd had the sense to have the car heater mended before she left London. Still. it couldn't be too far to travel now, if she'd followed Aunt Meg's rather involved directions correctly. If she took it slowly she should manage without any accidents even with the windscreen teeming with hailstones.

Kate peered anxiously ahead down the country lane whose twists and turns she had been following for the last half hour, hoping desperately that she was heading in the right direction for Westford. In the half-light of the afternoon it was hard to get her bearings, although the broken-down farmhouse she had passed ten minutes ago must surely have been the one Aunt Meg had marked on the map. She supposed she should have stopped and asked for help.

It was too late to bother about that now. If this *was* the right way there should be a turning to the right just round the next corner. And there it was! Kate's spirits lifted and she edged the car slowly down the narrow lane, barely wide enough for two cars to pass each other, with growing confidence. Not long to go now before Aunt Meg would be giving Kate a warm welcome and fussing round her. It would be good to end the journey, she thought, shivering as she drove cautiously on.

As she approached the next twist in the lane she caught the hum of a car engine a little distance behind her and approaching at some speed. 'He ought to know better than to travel at that rate on roads like these,' Kate muttered to herself furiously. The words were hardly spoken before a car horn sounded harshly as a vehicle took the curve that she was rounding. It was almost upon her by the time she had wrenched frantically at the steering wheel in an attempt to get out of its path and avoid what seemed to be the inevitable collision. The other driver reacted equally quickly and, missing the Mini by inches, swerved at a crazy angle. The car smashed against a tree and landed a few yards away in a ditch at the other side of the road.

Kate stopped and was out of the car in a moment, crossing the lane to see what she could do to help. Considering the force with which the other car had avoided her its occupants would be lucky indeed to have escaped without serious injury. Her anxious glance revealed only one figure, a man, inside the car and, to judge from the way he was wrenching aside the restraining band of his seat belt, it seemed that he was not badly hurt. She breathed a sigh of relief as she moved forward to assist him in pushing the buckled front door aside so that he could step out into the road.

Mercifully he seemed to have survived the experience without a scratch. But it was instantly made clear to Kate that, if his person had escaped injury, his temper most certainly had not.

'What the hell do you think you were playing at? You could have killed us both, you stupid fool!'

Kate wasn't sure what reaction she had expected from the driver of the car that had come close to mowing her down, but the cold fury in his voice brought an instant response from her. 'What was *I* playing at?' she exploded. 'I think you're the one with some explaining to do. You were driving like a maniac! You should know better than to speed on roads like these.'

'And I suppose you consider the snail's pace at which you were travelling was more suited to public safety? If crawling along at ten miles an hour is your idea of a brisk pace, woman, it's time you went back to driving school.'

'As it happens,' Kate informed him sharply, 'my windscreen wipers aren't working and I was travelling as fast as I dared considering that I couldn't see too well in this downpour. I was in the right, and if you want my opinion——'

'Not particularly.' He cut her short and turned abruptly to examine the damage suffered by his car, leaving Kate standing in the middle of the road, indignation robbing her of words for an adequate reply to such rudeness. His voice, coldly sarcastic, floated back to her. 'And, if you've got the safety of your fellow travellers so much at heart, it might be an idea to stop blocking the road. The next traveller to come along might not be as good at avoiding you as I was.' His tone indicated a certain hope that this might be the case. 'I think that causing one accident ought to be enough for you tonight, don't you?'

Arrogant swine, Kate thought, nevertheless moving hastily to stand on the edge of the ditch. The driving sleet, which showed no sign of letting up, quickly soaked through her clothes, already damp from her last encounter with the elements. She shivered violently, feeling colder and more bedraggled at that moment than she had ever done in her life before.

The stranger was bending over the front wheels of his car, which were twisted at a crazy angle and buried firmly in the mud of the ditch. Kate studied him warily. A first glance had given her only a quick impression of a giant of a man who had towered menacingly over her. Now, with the leisure to inspect him more closely, she realised that he must indeed be well over six feet tall and powerfully built. Without that disagreeable expression on his face, she mused, he'd be almost good-looking. Always supposing one's taste inclined to dark-haired men. Jeremy was fair-haired and blue-eyed, with the sort of boyish charm that had bowled over every woman he had met. If the stranger was capable of charm, thought Kate wryly, he didn't seem to think that she merited its use. He'd learn soon enough that these cave-men tactics wouldn't get him anywhere! She stamped her feet in a vain attempt to keep warm and wondered how long she would have to wait before he delivered some kind of verdict on the damage.

'Have you no sense at all?' The stranger's tall figure loomed in front of her again. Apparently his inspection of his battered car was now completed and his irritable voice roused Kate from her stupor of cold. 'Why the hell didn't you get back in your car and wait for me out of the rain?'

It would serve you right if I got in the car and drove off, she thought viciously. I wonder how you'd have managed. Instead she told him, making a valiant effort to keep her temper, 'I thought there might be something I could do.'

'Did you?' His contempt stung her. 'I think you've done a little too much already, so you'll understand if I don't take you up on your kind offer of help.' And, as she opened her mouth to reply, he said impatiently, 'For God's sake, stop arguing and let's get out of the cold.'

His words made some sense, Kate admitted, and she submitted to being bustled across the road and into the shelter of her own car. Safely ensconced on the front seat beside her, he stripped off his expensive-looking driving gloves, which, Kate noted with some satisfaction, were covered with dirt and mud, and ordered her briskly, 'Get the heater on, will you, or would you like to try and kill me of cold now?'

'I've told you that it wasn't my fault——'

'All right, forget it,' he said wearily. 'I've enough problems without arguing the toss with you all night over who was to blame. Just put the heater on before we both freeze.'

It gave Kate no small pleasure to tell him, 'It doesn't work.'

He swore under his breath and when he spoke again she could tell it was costing him an effort not to lose his temper. 'You'd better get me to a phone as quickly as possible so that I can contact a garage and get a breakdown truck here.'

'I keep a tow-rope in the boot for emergencies,' Kate suggested, glad at last to have a chance to prove herself other than the fool he so obviously considered her. 'Couldn't we try using that?'

'My dear Miss—Mrs——?'

'Miss. Sherwood. Kate Sherwood.'

'My dear Miss Sherwood,' he spoke as if addressing a not very bright five-year-old, 'it will take a heavy truck to drag my car out of that mud, and then it's a write-off until the steering column's fixed. What I require, as I believe I've already told you once, is a local garage with a decent breakdown service. Do you think it's within your limited powers to get me to one?'

'Yes, of course. I see what you mean. But there's really no need to speak to me as if I'm an idiot or something.'

'I generally speak as I find,' he commented nastily.

'I was only trying to help.'

'Heaven preserve us,' he muttered, and turned to free the buckle of his seat belt which was caught up in the door.

Presented with the back of his arrogant head, Kate fought the temptation to throw something at him. The sooner she drove this boorish stranger to the nearest phone and deposited him there to make his own arrangements, the better it would be for both of them. He obviously didn't consider her any use at all to him. Well, that was all right by her! she decided. She forced herself to enquire in a reasonably neutral tone where he would like to be driven.

'How should I know?' was the irritable response. 'I'm a stranger here.'

Definitely not the moment to try his temper by admitting that she had only the vaguest idea where she might be at this precise point. Kate thought swiftly. Should she reverse and try to find that broken-down place she had passed some time before? Perhaps there wouldn't be a phone there and she might miss the house in the dark. She could think of few more unattractive fates than getting lost in the wilderness of narrow lanes which she had so recently negotiated. Better to travel on and look for a farm or cottage somewhere off the road ahead. At least they would be driving in what she hoped was the direction of Westford.

It took three attempts to start the car and, although the stranger forbore to comment, she was aware of his impatience. Silence yawned between them. Hardly an occasion for making small talk. Kate couldn't help smiling at the thought of exchanging platitudes about the weather with the arrogant man by her side.

'I'd hardly have thought the mess we're in is a laughing matter.' His disagreeable tones cut in on her reflections. 'Or are you given to smiling vacantly instead of concentrating on your driving?'

She ignored that sally and he lapsed into silence again. The next few minutes passed in comparative peace, although Kate was all too conscious of the critical figure beside her, causing her to make mistakes, do silly things that she would normally never have done. By way of excuse she told him, 'I'm really quite a good driver. I don't know what's got into me tonight.'

'Indeed?'

She fumed inwardly. Let him make just one more crack like that, just one more sarcastic comment and——

'Stop a few yards ahead on the right. There's a light shining. It looks as if it might be a farm or something.' His eyes, keener than hers, had spotted a building some distance away. 'Wait here,' he ordered her. 'I'll go and investigate.'

'I'll come too!'

'No point two of us getting drenched,' he said firmly, ignoring the fact that Kate was already soaked to the skin. 'I'll be back.' The door slammed and he was gone, swallowed up in the darkness before she could argue further.

'Arrogant, domineering swine!' she shouted after him. Although the object of the insult was already too far away to hear it, it gave her a certain amount of relief from the pent-up tension which had gripped her throughout her encounter with the stranger. Of course it wouldn't occur to him that she might have better things to do than meekly await his bidding. Overbearing brute! It would serve him right if she decided to drive off into the darkness and leave him. She wondered how he would react if he came back and found her gone. It was a tempting idea, but she abandoned it reluctantly. If there wasn't a phone at this house, she supposed it was her duty to drive him on until he found somewhere he could summon help. And, her conscience told her, although it hadn't been her fault that the accident had happened, perhaps she was slightly in the wrong ...

The rain seemed to be slackening at last, although she could still feel the wind buffeting the car from all sides. A trickle of water ran down her neck and she wriggled uncomfortably. God knows what *he* would say if he found that the roof of the car leaked as well as all its other defects. At least Aunt Meg wouldn't be worrying over her non-appearance. Kate had made it clear that she would be taking the journey in easy stages. 'I'm not out to break any records,' she had written to her, 'so expect me when you see me.' The thought of Aunt Meg's loving welcome and with it the prospect of food, a hot bath and a bed for the night was absolute bliss.

A noise at the car door roused her from a pleasant vision of home comforts. An icy draught blew into the car as the stranger's wet form eased itself inside.

'They've no phone, but suggest that we drive on to the nearest village, which is called Westford, where there's a garage which may be able to help. Apparently we're only a mile or so from it, so it's hardly worth our while trying to phone from anywhere else. They offered us coffee or a hot meal, but I told them we hadn't time to stop.'

High-handed as ever. Kate cursed him silently. 'It

wouldn't occur to you to consult me about that, I suppose?' she asked coldly.

'No, Miss Sherwood, it didn't occur to me. My time's too vital to waste at the moment. And where I'm concerned time is money. I'm due back in London for an urgent meeting tonight and the sooner I'm on my way there the better.'

'And what I think is of no account?'

'I assumed that you would prefer to spend no more time in my company than was strictly necessary.' His tone was bland. 'Wasn't I right in doing so?'

'Perfectly right,' said Kate, gritting her teeth and driving on.

The short distance to the village of Westford was covered with reasonable speed and, once there, the garage, the only one which the village possessed, was easy to locate. Kate drew up outside it with a flourish. Her relief at getting rid of her unwelcome passenger was intense, but she made an effort to be pleasant as she said goodbye to him.

'I hope everything is settled all right and you don't have to wait too long for your car to be mended,' she said brightly, holding out her hand in polite farewell.

He ignored the gesture. 'Count yourself lucky that I've neither the time nor the inclination to pursue the matter. Otherwise you might find yourself facing a heavy bill for damage to my car. Still, I suppose you did your best to make amends, so I'm prepared to forget the matter.'

'How dare you!' Kate finally lost the battle to keep her temper. 'So you're prepared to forget the matter. How very gracious of you. You couldn't be more eager to forget the matter than I am. I've never met such a rude, overbearing, completely selfish man. The only consolation is that I'm never likely to meet anyone worse than you however long I search!'

'This is hardly the time for a public slanging match.'

'I'm not likely to have another chance to tell you what I think of you. I never want to see you again—and thank God I'm not likely to!'

It seemed that her last insult had fallen on deaf ears as he extricated himself from the front seat of the Mini and ignored her. But, once on the pavement, he held the door open and turned back to speak to her. 'It seems that at last we've found a subject on which we do agree, Miss Sherwood. I think I could live for a long time without feeling any desire to see *you* again.'

He slammed the door shut and walked away without a backward glance.

CHAPTER TWO

'He was so rude! He didn't even have the common courtesy to thank me for rescuing him and driving him to the garage. He just walked off without a word of acknowledgement as if I was beneath his notice.' Not the precise truth, but Kate had no intention of repeating the stranger's hurtful parting words to anyone, not even Aunt Meg. Safely ensconced in an armchair in Aunt Meg's comfortable sitting-room with the horrors of the journey behind her, she was still fuming over her meeting on the road.

It had not taken her very long to find Aunt Meg's guest house in a community which seemed to consist of only a small cluster of houses and shops centred round the village square. 'You can't miss Glebe House,' Aunt Meg had written with the airy assurance of one who knew the place well. After following her aunt's involved directions of the route to the village and being convinced that they had added miles to her journey, Kate expected a lengthy tour of the village before she found the right house. In fact, despite the gloom in the narrow turnings off the main square, she had no difficulty in locating the house with its weatherbeaten sign at the door announcing 'Bed and Breakfast'.

It had been a relief to be greeted at last by Aunt Meg, a small, grey-haired woman, whose deceptive air of fragility concealed more energy and ability to organise than anyone Kate had ever known. She had been shocked by her guest's bedraggled appearance and, treating her much as she had done in the days when Kate had been a tomboyish eight-year-old, forever falling out of trees and into duckponds, had allowed her no time to explain what had happened to her before despatching her firmly up the stairs to take a hot bath. 'Time enough to tell me all about it later,' she told Kate. 'We don't want you going down with pneumonia or worse at the start of your holidays. Don't go bothering about unpacking your cases now. There's a clean towel on the rail in the bathroom and you can use that dressing-gown of mine that's hanging behind the door. It's old, but it's clean and it'll keep you warm enough for the moment.' And Aunt Meg had disappeared to the kitchen to arrange some supper for her.

Kate emerged from the bathroom a little later restored from a shivering wreck to something approaching her normal self and now, with a tray of hot food on her lap, she sat relishing the warmth of the blazing log fire. As she ate she offered Aunt Meg a slightly expurgated version of her encounter with the disagreeable man who had caused her to be so late.

'He blamed me for every single thing that went wrong,' she said indignantly. 'And he couldn't resist making sarcastic comments about anything I did to try and help.'

'He does sound rather an ill-mannered character, dear,' her aunt agreed. 'But I expect he was worried about his car and getting it on the road again.' Aunt Meg always liked to think the best of everyone and, true to form, it was not long before she sprang to the stranger's defence.

'That's no excuse for bad manners.'

'No, dear, but you did say he seemed to be in a terrible hurry,' Aunt Meg persisted. 'And it can't have been pleasant coping with an accident to his car in weather like this.'

'I rather thought *I* coped with it,' Kate objected. 'I drove him to find a garage, which was remarkably kind of me considering how disagreeable he was and that the accident was all the fault of *his* dangerous driving.'

'And that's another thing,' her aunt continued calmly. 'Men do so like to be in command of the situation. I expect he resented having to rely on a female to help him.'

'Oh, he did,' said Kate, recalling the stranger's fury as she had attempted to calm him down.

'Well, there you are. You can't really blame the poor man if he lost his temper a little.'

'Poor man!' Kate snorted. 'He should have thanked his lucky stars that I was prepared to help him. Aunt Meg, have you never heard of Women's Lib?'

'Yes, and a lot of nonsense it is too,' her aunt told her firmly. 'As I'm sure you'll find out for yourself soon enough when you've a man of your own to care for.'

'I'll cross that bridge when I come to it,' Kate said hastily, trying to sound casual and wondering how to steer the conversation away from a discussion of her marriage prospects. Aunt Meg had married young and, having enjoyed over forty years of married bliss with Uncle Walter, never hesitated to recommend marriage as an ideal state. Kate knew that the fact that she had reached the advanced age of twenty-four without yet having contemplated marriage to any one of the young men she had been out with was a great disappointment to her aunt. Thank goodness she hadn't written to tell her about Jeremy's proposal.

'Don't think I don't approve of young girls training for a career and getting out to see the world a little,' Aunt Meg went on. 'But I know there's no job anywhere to compare with looking after your husband. And children too, if you're lucky.' Aunt Meg's one regret was that she had never been able to have a family. Kate had always suspected, from the keen interest she had shown in her over the years, that Aunt Meg had come to look upon her as the daughter she had never had.

'Aunt Meg, I am not, positively not, going to debate the role of women in society with you.' She smiled affectionately at the older woman. 'We'd only end up going round in circles the way we usually do. You can make any excuse you like for that horrid man and I won't contradict you. I'm just relieved to be here at last and to see you again.'

Successfully sidetracked by Kate's last remark, Aunt Meg looked pleased. 'It's good of you to come and visit me, dear, although what on earth you'll find to do here I really don't know.'

'Don't worry, Aunt Meg. Peace and quiet will be fine,' Kate assured her. 'A few long country walks, lots of your good cooking, and, most important, a chance to recover from being worked to death at the office.'

'And how will your boss manage without you?'

'Mr Edwards? Oh, he'll get by, I expect.' Kate shrugged, wondered for a brief moment whether to conceal her resignation, then decided there was no point in keeping quite about it. She didn't like the thought of responding with a tissue of lies to Aunt Meg's kindly queries about her work and how she was liking it. 'Actually, I gave my notice in last week, Aunt Meg. I'll be looking for another job when I get back to London, but I'd been overdoing it a bit and I decided to give myself a good break first. There won't be any problems about finding something—trained secretaries are still in high demand, thank goodness.' She changed the subject swiftly, hoping to avoid awkward questions about her reasons for leaving her present job. 'At least I'll be able to help you with the housework and let you have a rest for a while, won't I?'

'There's no need to be worrying about that,' her aunt said firmly. 'You're here for a holiday. Anyway, it's only in the summer that I'm run off my feet looking after the tourists. It's quite amazing how many of them we get in such a small village. I usually have one of the girls from the village to help out with the cooking and cleaning at the height of the season and generally we manage things very well between us. Out of season I don't bother too much. I don't actually bar the door to visitors, but I'm lucky if I see a strange face from one month to the next at this time of year.'

As if to give the lie to her words there was a sudden, insistent ring on the doorbell. Aunt Meg glanced at the clock, then started to her feet looking puzzled. 'Who on earth can that be at this time of night?' she wondered, and left the room to find out. Kate heard the front door open and shut and then the sound of voices in the hall.

'If you'd like to put your cases over there——' Aunt Meg sounded more than a little flustered. 'Of course you will realise that I don't really cater for guests out of season. But the rooms are all ready and it won't take me long to make up a bed for you.' A doubtful note crept into her voice and Kate wondered if she was having second thoughts about accommodating the unexpected arrival. 'Perhaps you'd prefer me to show you the room before you make up your mind?'

'I hardly think that will be necessary. I'm sure everything will be fine. I'm very grateful to you for putting me up at such short notice,' came a masculine voice reassuring her.

It was a voice which carried a note of confident assurance. A voice that Kate recognised only too easily, although she had heard it for the first time only three hours or so before. She put her empty tray on the floor beside her and got hurriedly to her feet, hoping against hope that she was wrong. Surely he wouldn't plague her here too? But the tall figure entering the room in the wake of her aunt was unmistakable.

'Kate, this gentleman is stranded in the village for the night, so he'll be staying here. Mr Blake, this is my niece, Kate, who is on holiday and visiting me. She——'

'Miss Sherwood and I already know each other,' he interposed smoothly. His expression did not suggest that he was in any way overjoyed to renew his acquaintance with her.

Not unnaturally Aunt Meg jumped to the wrong conclusion. 'That's nice,' she said cheerfully. 'Isn't that a coincidence? I suppose you met in London?'

'No. We met on the road to Westford, Aunt Meg,' Kate said with icy calm. 'This *gentleman* is the one I was telling you about, whose car went into the ditch.' If looks could have killed, she thought, he'd be lying dead at my feet by now instead of staring at me as if I'd just crawled out from under a stone.

There was no support forthcoming from Aunt Meg, who seemed to be completely overwhelmed by the advent of such an unexpected visitor. 'You must be frozen,' she exclaimed in horrified tones. 'You must get by the fire and get warm. Here, let me take your coat. It can dry by the kitchen range while I'm getting your room ready for you.'

He shrugged off his wet overcoat and handed it to Aunt Meg with a brief word of thanks.

'I'll come and help you, Aunt Meg,' Kate offered hastily, appalled at the prospect of being left to make polite conversation with their guest.

'No, dear, thanks all the same. Pour Mr Blake a glass of whisky, would you? It's the best cure I know for the cold and there's a bottle over there in the cupboard.' Promising not to be long, Aunt Meg left the room.

Alone with Kate, he walked over to the fire and stood, hands outstretched, gazing down at the flames. He seemed lost in thought and quite oblivious of her presence. She took the opportunity to study him more closely.

She had to concede to herself that he was a man whom most women would find attractive, despite, or perhaps because of, his general air of being someone who knew exactly what he wanted out of life and was used to acquiring it, whatever the odds. Well over six feet tall, his formal grey suit served only to emphasise his height and his lean, powerful figure. It was hard to guess his age, but she judged him to be somewhere in his late thirties, although there was, as yet, no hint of grey in his dark hair. A firm chin, with a hint of obstinacy about the mouth. And his eyes were——

His eyes were a glacial shade of grey, she discovered, and could convey a freezing stare of displeasure.

'I hope you'll recognise me if we ever have the misfortune to meet again.'

It appeared that he had decided to acknowledge her existence again, if only to rebuke her for staring at him. Kate struggled for composure. Why was it that he always seemed to catch her out?

'I'm sorry,' she stumbled weakly in an effort to apologise. 'I really didn't mean—I——'

'What about that glass of whisky your aunt so kindly offered me?' he asked, brushing aside her feeble attempts to excuse her behaviour with a brief, authoritative wave of his hand. 'I rather think I deserve a stiff drink after all I've had to suffer tonight.'

'I'll get you some.' Kate ignored the gibe and crossed the room to find him the drink. As she stretched up to open the cupboard door she could feel his gaze upon her and she was suddenly aware that Aunt Meg's dressing gown, which she had been forced to wear until she had time to unpack her own, was scarcely an adequate covering. Aunt Meg was a tiny woman, barely five foot tall, and what had reached to a respectable, below-the-knee length on her barely stretched to mid-thigh on Kate, five foot seven in her stockinged feet and built on more generous lines. Still, after all that had happened, she could hardly suppose that he saw her in any other light than that of a nuisance. She found the bottle of whisky and poured a liberal amount into a tumbler for him.

'Would you like some water with this?'

'No, thanks.'

As she offered him the glass her fingers brushed against his and she recoiled slightly. She hoped that he hadn't noticed the action, but this man noticed everything.

'You're quite safe for the moment,' he told her nastily. 'I admit that I wanted nothing more than to wring your neck a little while ago, but, fortunately for you, the impulse seems to have passed.' He took a long drink of the whisky and then set the glass down. 'I usually try to remember my manners—even in the company of overgrown schoolgirls such as yourself.'

Kate glared at him, her fear of him momentarily forgotten. 'I'm twenty-four.'

'Indeed?' His tone suggested faint disbelief.

She had never met anyone who could knock the wind out of her sails so successfully. She retreated to her armchair by the side of the fire and fought to keep her temper. There was a brief silence and she was conscious that he was studying her, his piercingly critical gaze probing every part of her, from the top of her tousled chestnut hair to her long, bare legs. His glance lingered on the neckline of her gown, loosely tied and giving a sight of the creamy curve of her throat and the shadowy promise of her breasts.

'My apologies,' he said. His eyes mocked her harshly. 'I can see now that I was mistaken.'

She had feigned indifference to his scrutiny, but, at his

words, moved nervously in her chair, drawing the gown more firmly round her. The derisive light in his eyes showed that he had noted the action.

'I did say that you were safe for the moment,' he reminded her softly. 'Are you scared I might demand compensation for all the trouble you've caused me?'

'I'm sorry about your car,' Kate muttered.

'So you should be. But having my car out of action for God knows how long is a mere trifle compared with the fact that it's all due to you that I've missed an important business meeting, which may have cost me thousands of pounds.'

Kate had had enough of apologising. She'd made the effort, but it seemed that he was ignoring the gesture. She couldn't help feeling that, if he'd missed his meeting, it served him right. She gave him a sweet smile and pointed out, reasonably enough, 'Considering the rate you were travelling at, it strikes me you were in danger of missing your meeting anyway. If you'd started off in plenty of time I don't suppose any of this would have happened.'

'That's got nothing at all to do with it.'

She ignored him and continued defiantly, 'And it's no use demanding any compensation, because I haven't got any money.'

His smile gave her a sudden feeling of unease. 'Did I say anything about money? There's such a thing as payment in kind.'

What did he mean? Kate had a notion that it might be safer not to stay around to find out. This conversation was getting decidedly out of hand. Somehow she managed to get to her feet. 'I think I'd better go and see if my aunt wants me to help her. If you'll excuse me, Mr Blake——'

'Running away from me?' he mocked her. 'You know

your aunt said she didn't need any help.' He was standing in front of her, blocking her way to the door.

'Will you let me pass, please?' she asked, and made to sidestep him and reach the door. In her haste to get away from him she forgot the abandoned tray lying on the floor and, catching her foot on its edge, would have fallen if a strong grip had not caught her and held her up.

'You didn't answer my question,' he told her, tightening his hold on her and drawing her nearer to him without apparent effort despite her almost frantic struggles to be set free. His face was only inches from hers and it was a disturbing closeness. 'Don't you think you ought to say something?' he taunted her softly, and, as she gazed helplessly at him, her lips parted for an indignant reply, he bent his head towards her and kissed her hard.

For a brief instant of stunned shock Kate remained quiescent in his arms. Then, as the urgent pressure of his mouth on hers increased, she fought desperately to escape from him. But it was no use; he would set her free when it suited him and not before, and he was determined to punish her. His arms felt like steel bands around her, tightening, mocking her attempts to break free as he gathered her still closer, moulding her to him and making her aware of the hard, unyielding strength of his body. His lips on hers were compelling, demanding a response which she fought hard to refuse him. Yet, in spite of herself, she found that she was weakening, succumbing to the assault he was making on her senses. The ability to struggle was leaving her, draining away and making her strangely vulnerable. She knew she couldn't fight him any longer: she must give in to him.

Then, as violently as he had seized her, he released her again and she staggered back from him, one hand going instinctively to her bruised mouth, which still seemed to bear the pressure of his lips.

'That'll teach you not to provoke me again,' he said with some satisfaction.

'How dare you!'

'Can't you think of a more original response than that?' He seemed unmoved, even slightly amused by her words. 'You'll be trying to slap my face next.'

She was sorely tempted to do just that, predictable behaviour or no, but the thought of the effortless way he had mastered her struggles gave her pause. She had no way of knowing how he might retaliate if she tried anything of the sort and, for the moment at least, she had no intention of finding out. Instead, feeling as if her legs could hardly support her, she sat down again.

'Very wise,' he mocked her. He bent down to retrieve the scattered dishes and stacked them on the tray. 'I think I'd better put these out of harm's way, don't you? We don't want any more accidents.'

He picked up the load and put it on a small table by the door, then returned to stand by the fire. Kate maintained what she hoped was a dignified silence, but it seemed that she had failed to convince him of her utter indifference to his actions.

'You needn't look so apprehensive,' he said with some amusement. 'I should have warned you I'm a dangerous man to cross. But, as I said, you provoked me. I shan't be repeating the experience. At least,' he qualified with a half smile, 'if you behave yourself.'

'Do you normally force your attentions on women who annoy you?'

He sounded as if the conversation suddenly bored him. 'I don't usually need to force my attentions, as you put it, on any woman. I invariably find most of them are only too happy to—oblige me.'

'Then I suppose I must be unique in not being swept off my feet by you,' Kate said recklessly. 'Perhaps, in future, you'd better confine yourself to delighting those poor fools who can take such insufferable behaviour.'

She had no chance to hear what reply he intended to this sally, for at that moment the door opened and Aunt Meg entered.

'I hope Kate has been looking after you properly, Mr Blake?' she asked anxiously. 'I'm sorry to have taken so long to get your room ready for you.'

'Oh, I'm not complaining, Mrs Carmichael,' he said. 'Your niece has certainly done her best to entertain me in your absence.'

Kate caught the undercurrent of amusement in his voice and seethed. How dare he laugh at her? She tried to calm down, aware that losing her temper with him was not the way to deal with this man. She needed to keep all her wits about her if she wanted to come off best in any encounter with him.

'You'll be wanting a meal, I expect, Mr Blake?' Her aunt was fussing over him anxiously. If this was the tender care afforded to all the summer visitors, Kate was hardly surprised that so many of them returned year after year to stay with Aunt Meg. She had a strong suspicion, however, that this was not the case and that Aunt Meg had succumbed to the stranger's attractive face and air of command. 'I'm afraid it'll only be very makeshift,' she was saying worriedly, 'but I could heat up some soup, if you——'

'I have eaten, thanks. But a cup of coffee would be nice, if that's possible?'

He could be charming, when the mood took him, Kate thought sourly, as she saw her aunt respond to his smile.

'Of course.'

'Sit down, Aunt Meg. I'll see to the coffee.' Kate was on her feet in an instant, seizing her opportunity to get away from this disagreeable man and the strange effect he was having upon her nervous system. She liked to think that she was in complete control of any situation in which she found herself and was not used to the state of impotent rage which had come upon her all too often in the last few hours. She needed to have a short breathing space to think clearly again. if only he hadn't to make it quite obvious from the look he directed at her that he knew only too well why she was retiring to the kitchen.

'But you don't know where I keep anything——' her aunt began in mild protest.

'I'll find my way around. Don't worry.' Kate was out of the room and had closed the door firmly behind her before the older woman could argue any further.

As she crossed the hall into the kitchen she caught sight of his luggage piled at the foot of the stairs and resisted the impulse to vent her feelings by kicking the smooth pigskin cases. To judge from the variety of gaudy foreign labels which adorned them there could be few countries of the world that their owner had yet to favour with his presence. A well-used briefcase, bulging at the seams, lay beside them. Following an urge that she could not have explained, Kate bent to look at them more closely, casting a fearful glance behind her at the closed door of the sitting room as she did so. How would she excuse her behaviour if he were suddenly to appear and catch her examining his cases like some amateur detective?

In the event a few seconds close study revealed no further information than the fact that the dictatorial stranger's forename was Nicholas and his address was a fashionable London one.

Nicholas Blake. The name sounded vaguely familiar and she wondered where she could have heard it before. In the newspapers perhaps? He was obviously a high-powered, successful type. The gossip columns? No, despite his arrogant remarks about his success with women she couldn't see him as part of the fashionable set. They would bore him. Kate couldn't place him. That she had never met him before, she was quite sure—it would have been impossible to have encountered such a forceful character and not be aware of it in every tingling nerve of her body. Dislike him she might, but he was the sort of man whom it was impossible to dismiss as a nonentity. He would stamp his personality on everyone with whom he came into contact, whatever the situation.

Kate entered the kitchen with a slight feeling of disappointment that she had not turned up any further facts about him. Not that she could care less about him as a man, she told herself defensively, but it would occur to anyone to wonder what such a well-travelled businessman found to interest him in such an out-of-the-way place in the middle of November. Work—or pleasure? Whichever it was it seemed urgent to judge from the speed at which he had been driving. Or perhaps that was his normal method of travelling? As if it could supply an answer to her questions she scowled resentfully at the heavy overcoat which Aunt Meg had draped across a chair to dry in front of the stove.

It did not take her long to discover where everything was kept and in a few moments she had filled the kettle and put it on to boil and set out the coffee cups. No doubt *he* preferred some exotic blend of coffee, she thought, as she carried the tray out of the kitchen. It would do him good to sample instant and see how the other half lived for a change!

Aunt Meg seemed to be getting on well with him. She turned and smiled proudly as Kate entered the room.

'Kate has a very high-powered job in London, Mr Blake,' she confided to him.

Oh dear, the wretched man probably knew her life history by now, she thought ruefully. She hoped it had bored him profoundly.

'Indeed?'

The sarcasm in his voice made Kate squirm. How dared he assume on the evidence of one encounter that she was some kind of brainless idiot? She busied herself pouring coffee, wishing as she handed him his cup that she could have thrown it in his arrogant face instead. Aunt Meg, suddenly conscious of an atmosphere that she did not understand, was looking at her anxiously and she forced herself to act normally. She had no intention of giving Nicholas Blake the further satisfaction of making her lose control of herself again.

She turned to him and asked with assumed concern, 'Will the garage be able to repair your car, Mr Blake?'

If she expected to disconcert him she had failed. He followed her lead with just the right amount of polite response. 'Not tonight, I'm afraid. The mechanic drove out with me to have a look at the damage, but what with the weather and the fact that their breakdown truck was already out on another job, there wasn't much that could be done. They'll tow it in to the garage tomorrow morning and see what can be done then.'

Aunt Meg clucked sympathetically. 'You weren't able to hire a car at all?'

He shrugged. 'I was hoping to do that once I'd got my luggage from the car, but none of the firms I phoned from the garage were able to offer me anything for tonight, so I gave up in the end and decided to spend the night here.'

'How very vexing for you! But it's really no night to be travelling,' Aunt Meg consoled him.

'And what lucky chance led you to Glebe House, I wonder, Mr Blake?' Kate asked coldly. 'I'd hardly have thought that a place like this would come up to your high standards.'

'Kate, really!' Her aunt was shocked at such rudeness, but the object of the attack ignored it. She wished she could have withdrawn the remark; it was so clearly what he would have expected from an overgrown schoolgirl like herself. He turned to her aunt to give an explanation.

'I stopped at the Red Lion for something to eat, but they weren't able to put me up for the night. The landlord directed me here. He was sure you would take pity on me.'

He smiled at Aunt Meg and, watching him, Kate was surprised at the difference it made to his face, relaxing the rather hard mouth and bringing a much-needed warmth to his eyes. If she had met him under other circumstances she might well have found him rather a pleasant man. She remembered Jane, who had considered it her clear duty to educate her less sophisticated flat-mate in the ways of the world, telling her solemnly, 'It's all very well to talk about not getting to know a man until you've lived with him. Believe me, you don't know what any man's like until he's lost his temper with you a couple of times.' Well, on that basis, she supposed that she was certainly on the way to a good understanding of Nicholas Blake. If indeed she wanted one.

He accepted another cup of coffee and chatted for a while to Aunt Meg, asking questions about the guest house and life in the country, apparently content to listen to tales of summer visitors. Apart from the occasional comment which he directed towards her he largely ignored Kate, and she was relieved that he did so. *He* might be capable of treating what had passed between them as an everyday occurrence, but she certainly wouldn't recover from the experience for quite some time. She could still feel the insistent demand of his mouth on hers and the effect it had had upon her.

She roused herself, suddenly aware that their visitor was getting to his feet.

'It's late, Mrs Carmichael. I mustn't keep you up.' He bade Kate a casual 'goodnight' as he left the room and she gave a sigh of relief as her aunt followed him to show him to his room. Thank goodness that was over!

When Aunt Meg returned, however, it seemed that she didn't share her views.

'What a *pleasant* man Mr Blake is. So appreciative of everything. He even apologised for putting me to so much trouble,' she told Kate.

'Which was more than he did to me when I drove him to the garage.' Kate didn't feel inclined to tell her aunt that their guest had kissed her. Perhaps if she ignored the action she would forget it had ever happened. But she doubted it somehow. 'Sorry, Aunt Meg, we'll have to agree to differ on Mr Blake. I think he's a typical male chauvinist—charming when he's getting what he wants and a complete bear when he's thwarted. I've met his sort a thousand times.'

But was Nicholas Blake so easy to dismiss? she wondered, as, later that night in the cosy room that Aunt Meg had assigned her, she tossed and turned, endlessly reliving the events of the day in all their humiliating detail. She had never met anyone who had treated her the way he had presumed to deal with her. Just who did he think he was? As an efficient secretary Kate prided herself on her ability to cope with all kinds of people and keep her head. But she had known instinctively that here was a man who could not be classified as anything but dangerous to handle and she hadn't been able to cope. She went over every word of their conversation again, wondering what she could have said or done to deflate him, and came to the conclusion that nothing would have dented *that* massive ego.

But did it matter that she had come off decidedly the worse for the encounter? She supposed it didn't, just as long as he left her life next morning as abruptly as he had entered it and she never laid eyes on him again! Surely that wasn't too much to ask, she was thinking, as sleep finally claimed her.

CHAPTER THREE

KATE overslept the next morning. She was eventually awakened by the noise of a car backfiring outside the window. The sounds of activity from downstairs and a quick glance at the travelling alarm clock by her bedside revealed that it was horribly late. Nine o'clock already! What must Aunt Meg be thinking of her? She sprang out of bed, made her way to the bathroom for a hasty wash and, back in the bedroom again, hunted through her case for something to wear. She had hung up yesterday's once smart trouser suit in the faint hope that it might recover from the drenching it had received, but it still looked a sad wreck.

Another crime to lay at Nicholas Blake's door, she thought angrily as she found a bright red sweater and a pair of scruffy but serviceable jeans. There was no point in dressing up if she was going to be helping Aunt Meg around the house. Besides, she had no intention of letting that man think that here was another woman who had fallen victim of his charms and who was out to attract him! Although she supposed even a man of his obvious self-conceit would be hard put to imagine that he had made a conquest of *her*.

Once dressed she ran a comb hastily through her hair and then headed in search of Aunt Meg—and some breakfast—half-hoping that by now their visitor would have been up and breakfasted long ago. Perhaps he might even have gone. But halfway down the stairs the hope died as she caught sight of a tall figure standing in the hall and using the phone, his broad back towards her.

Nicholas Blake appeared to be giving orders to someone and, from the sound of it, his temper had not been improved by a night's sleep. Or perhaps that irritable edge to his voice was his normal manner of communicating with the rest of mankind?

No, he was definitely angry about something. Kate halted, strangely reluctant to make him aware of her presence by squeezing past him on her way to the dining room.

'For God's sake, stop asking idiotic questions! I'm fully aware that I'm due in a meeting in an hour.' There was a pause and Kate could hear an agitated voice arguing at the other end. 'No, I don't know when I'll be back. Well, call Sir Geoffrey and explain I can't make it after all. Find some excuse. It'll do him good to kick his heels for a while. Use your head for a change. Isn't that what I pay you to do?' The telephone receiver rocked back on the cradle with considerable force and he turned, his expression thunderous. When he caught sight of Kate, apparently rooted to a spot halfway down the stairs, his face grew, if anything, slightly more grim. Obviously she wasn't forgiven yet for the trouble she had caused him.

He was dressed less formally this morning, his business suit discarded in favour of dark, well-fitting slacks and a black roll-neck sweater, but that air of impatient command which she had so resented the day before, the easy assurance of a man who was accustomed to getting his own way, remained. She had never met the man who could intimidate her, but Nicholas Blake seemed to manage it without even trying. She leapt into nervous speech.

'I'm sorry. I was coming downstairs—I couldn't help overhearing what you were saying. I hope it wasn't anything too private. I——' She was talking too much, too quickly, and only making things worse. Why did this man give her the feeling that she had to defend herself?

He shrugged. 'I don't normally conduct confidential business over a public phone.'

He stood back, indicating that she should precede him to the dining room, and she complied, feeling suitably put in her place. Aunt Meg was there, busily laying out the breakfast dishes on the highly polished oak table. Kate's heart sank when she saw there were only two places set. She supposed Aunt Meg must have breakfasted hours ago. Her penalty for oversleeping was to have to conduct a strained conversation with a man whom she was beginning to dislike more with every passing minute.

'I thought I heard you stirring, Kate,' her aunt smiled. 'No, don't worry—I don't need any help. Everything's ready. Mr Blake, did you manage to get through to your office? Your breakfast is all ready and it'll be with you in a minute.' She bustled out leaving Kate feeling strangely vulnerable.

He seemed to have no inclination to start up a conversation. He was standing by the window, studying with a preoccupied air the view of the mellow stone cottages and the village square beyond. It was a great temptation to ignore him, but Kate, for her sins, had been brought up to be polite. She searched desperately for a neutral topic of conversation.

'At least the weather's improved,' she ventured. An inept comment, particularly as the grey clouds scudding past the window gave no such indication. 'It's going to be brighter today.'

He turned impatiently. 'Is it? I'm glad you think so. I've just been to the garage to check up on my car. It seems I'm stranded in this godforsaken place for the best part of the morning at the very least. I hope you're pleased with yourself!'

The sound of the door opening checked Kate's impulse

to defend herself and she went forward to take the laden breakfast tray from her aunt, who retreated to the kitchen again, promising to return later for the empty dishes. 'There's more toast, if you want it,' she said, and went out, closing the door firmly behind her again.

They ate in silence for a while. His disagreeable mood didn't seem to have affected his appetite, she noted sourly, as she made an effort to eat her portion, eventually putting aside her plate in favour of a cup of steaming coffee. She asked him if he would like a cup, determined that he should not think that she was sulking.

'Please. Black with a dash of milk and no sugar.'

'Sweet enough, Mr Blake?' Kate couldn't resist the chance for a dig.

'So I've been told.' He raised a dark eyebrow quizzically. 'You wouldn't agree, of course.'

'No, and neither would your secretary, if the way you talked to her this morning was anything to go by.'

He looked amused. 'No man's a saint in his secretary's eyes. Surely you know that? She thinks she has me admirably trained. It does her good to be made to realise occasionally that she has no control over me at all.'

No, Kate certainly couldn't imagine him at the beck and call of any woman. He would be the dominant figure always, getting exactly what he required from any relationship, whether in business or in his private life. She wondered what happened to anyone who dared to challenge him. Presumably his powerful personality overwhelmed any resistance to his authority.

'And getting her to postpone your appointments at short notice and lie convincingly on your behalf is one way of demonstrating your power over her, is it?'

'That was hardly my fault,' he reminded her softly. 'Why all this sympathy for someone you've never met?

Don't waste your time bothering about my secretary. She'll cope.'

'You don't sound a very sympathetic boss,' she told him.

He shrugged. 'I expect my staff to be good at their jobs and I pay them accordingly. If they fall down on the job they leave. It's as simple as that.'

'And you're really foolish enough to think that you'll win their affection with an attitude like that?'

'I don't particularly care what they think about me,' he said with maddening superiority. 'But I do demand hard work and loyalty from the people I employ.'

'And do you always get what you demand, Mr Blake?' she asked him.

'Invariably.' He spoke with an easy assurance that made her long to wipe that smugness from his handsome face.

'You're mistaken. You can't buy people's loyalty. Haven't you discovered that yet? You may think that paying someone a good salary gives you the right to trample all over their feelings, but it doesn't, you know.'

'I wasn't aware that I'd claimed anything of the kind,' he said smoothly. 'But do go on with this rundown of my faults. I'm finding it interesting.'

Kate ignored the interruption. 'You owe a lot to the people who spend their time propping up your ego and making sure that you don't lose face in the business world and I advise you not to forget it. We're the ones who——' She broke off, aware that she had gone too far. But she meant every word she had said and didn't intend to retract them. She poured herself another cup of coffee, added milk and sugar, and stirred it defiantly as she waited for his anger to break about her head.

'You're speaking from personal experience, I suppose?' He sounded intrigued rather than annoyed. She was conscious of his grey eyes studying her curiously, analysing her with a directness that she found distinctly uncomfortable. 'Did someone trample on your feelings, Kate?'

'I don't remember saying that you could call me that, *Mr* Blake.'

'You didn't,' he said, unperturbed. 'But after last night I really feel we're on sufficiently intimate terms for me to take such a liberty.' As he spoke his eyes raked her face, dwelling for an instant too long on her lips and reminding her of the even greater liberty he had taken with her the previous night. She winced, living again the feeling of impotent weakness as she had struggled against him, the force of his masculine body pressing against hers and the pressure of his lips on hers. He was not finished with her yet. 'Don't you agree with me?' He knew the effect last night's little episode had had upon her and he was deliberately forcing her to recall the experience. How dared he?

'I don't think my personal life has anything to do with you,' she said, striving to be calm.

He ignored her, musing softly, 'Whoever he was, the man who took you for granted, the experience seems to have left you rather bitter.'

'I'd prefer to say slightly less gullible, I think, when it comes to dealing with your type.'

'We're not all tarred with the same brush, you know.'

'No?'

'You're very quick to condemn me,' he said. 'But you don't know me very well, do you?'

'I don't need to know you any better. You have the same attitude to life. You want your own way at all costs and you don't care who you crush in order to get it.'

'You make me sound very cold-blooded,' he commented.

'Aren't you?'

'I've been accused of ruthlessness on occasion,' he allowed. 'But I wouldn't say I had a reputation for being cold-blooded. Quite the contrary, in fact.'

She knew without him elaborating on the point that he was referring to his dealings with women. The conversation was leading to decidedly dangerous ground. Kate began to wish she had kept her mouth shut and not tangled with him. 'I'd rather not discuss the matter, if you don't mind,' she said desperately.

'I see. You prepare to abandon the battlefield when you're about to be proved wrong. How typically female!'

'Nothing of the sort, I just felt that the argument was getting a little too personal, that's all,' she fenced, hoping to deflect him.

'You mean,' he said calmly, 'that you're allowed to acuse me of being some domineering tyrant, straight out of Dickens, but I'm supposed to play the gentleman and not retaliate by telling you a few home truths. Well, it won't work with me. You picked the wrong man if you expected that kind of behaviour, Kate.' The amusement had vanished and there was a cruel note in his voice. She shivered, wondering what was coming next. 'You've as good as told me that I've no sympathy for anyone else's finer feelings, so you can hardly expect me to make an exception of you. Let's discuss him, shall we, this man who inspired such emotion? Who was he? Your boss? Your lover, perhaps?'

She wished she could block the taunting sound of his voice from her ears. Why had she got herself into this mess? She had only herself to blame. Nicholas Blake had warned her he was a difficult man to cross and if she hadn't learnt her lesson last night she could well believe it now. He was right, of course: she should never have let her feelings get the better of her. What right had she to attack him in the way she had done? On the grounds of their short acquaintance she might claim to dislike him, but she couldn't base her dislike on any deep knowledge of the man. Apart from the fact that he had a remarkably short temper, particularly where she was concerned, she knew absolutely nothing about him. Just because Jeremy had hurt her badly there was no excuse for assuming every successful businessman to be the same type.

He was watching her keenly. 'Had enough?' he asked her. Her face must have mirrored her thoughts. 'You're out of your depth, Kate, trying to take me on. You might as well admit it.'

Admit that he had got the better of her? Never! But if she didn't he would pursue the subject. 'I don't usually get so carried away.' She gave a shaky laugh. 'I'm not used to such impassioned arguments so early in the day.' If he cared to take that as an apology he was welcome to do so, provided that he abandoned his latest line of questioning.

'I'll agree with you there. I've never found the breakfast table the most suitable place for heated arguments.'

'You prefer to settle them in the boardroom?'

He gave her a sudden smile, the lighter expression transforming his rather sombre face and inviting her to respond to him. This man could charm when it suited him, she conceded that. 'When I argue with a woman I always find that the bedroom is the best place to settle matters.'

'I suppose you're usually successful there, too?' she asked, trying for a tone of sophisticated amusement.

'Perhaps you'd like to sample the experience some time?'

'Not particularly,' she said warily. 'I don't suppose either of us would enjoy the experiment.'

'You underestimate yourself, Kate. I'm sure I'd find it most rewarding.'

He had her at a loss again and he knew it. She searched for a witty reply and could only fight the temptation to throw the coffee pot at him. Grudgingly she accepted that when it came to this kind of verbal sparring he had the edge on her.

Fortunately he seemed disposed to move on to slightly less personal ground. 'Your aunt tells me you're on holiday. It seems a strange time of year to visit this part of the country. Or do you dislike sharing it with the tourists?'

She could have answered that his immaculate presence in the country was even stranger, but refrained. He was making an effort at small talk and anything was better than the exchange they had just been through. It was probably safer for both of them if she made an effort to be civil. 'I wanted to see Aunt Meg and this was as good a time as any to come. I'm a secretary and I'm between jobs at the moment.'

'If your typing's anything like your driving, I'm not surprised,' he commented caustically. 'Were you sacked or made redundant?'

'Neither. I resigned,' she told him haughtily, her good resolutions rapidly broken. What was it about him that made her react this way?

'I hope you had a good reason. Jobs are scarce these days. It's usually wise to decide where you're heading *before* you walk out. You may find it's a cruel, hard world when you start looking for another job.'

It had occurred to her to worry about finding another job, but she had pushed the thought to the back of her mind, determined to enjoy her visit to Aunt Meg before she considered the subject seriously. She had no intention of confiding her fears for the future to Nicholas Blake of all people. 'I'm an experienced secretary,' she said airily.

'I don't suppose I'll have much difficulty in getting another job.' She couldn't resist adding, 'The problem will be finding an employer I want to work for. There are so many high-handed, impossible bosses around.'

If the gibe registered, he ignored it as she might have known he would. 'So that explains your spirited defence of my poor Miss Wilkins. Where did you work?'

'Edwards Engineering.' She managed to say the name casually enough. 'You probably won't have heard of them. They're only a small firm——'

'Yes, I know them,' he interrupted her. 'They've just merged with Markham's outfit, haven't they?'

'You're very well informed.' Kate could not hide her surprise.

'I make it my business to be,' he said. 'So you left Edwards Engineering for reasons of your own which, no doubt, you've no intention of revealing to me. What next?'

'Why the sudden interest in my future prospects, Mr Blake?' If this relentless question and answer session passed for his idea of pleasant small talk, Kate preferred the Spanish Inquisition any day. 'Are you thinking of offering me a job?' she asked sweetly.

His gaze roved over her figure with insulting slowness before he chose to answer her. He could have been assessing a piece of prime beef on the hoof at a cattle market, thought Kate resentfully. 'I might be persuaded to find a use for you in some capacity or other.'

'Indeed?' Her temper was beginning to rise again.

'Yes. I suppose you've got other talents besides a vicious tongue and a sharp temper, although at present just what they might be escapes me.'

'You can save your breath,' she seethed. 'I don't think you need to worry about employing my talents or lack of them in your service. I'd rather starve in the street than work for you!'

He was unmoved by the outburst. 'Fine words. But if, as I suspect you will, you think better of that rather childish display of temper, you may still consider yourself free to get in touch with me.' He reached in his pocket and produced a business card which he tossed across the table to her. 'You never know, you might catch me in a philanthropic mood.' He pushed aside his chair and, his breakfast finished, prepared to get up.

She picked up the square of cardboard and, without even stopping to consider the action, tore it in two and threw the pieces back at him. 'Does that make it quite clear what I think of your offer, *Mr* Blake?'

'Perfectly.' His features were cold, his eyes narrowed as he looked at her and she sensed that, for once, his temper was being held firmly in check. 'I do hope you don't live to regret that action.'

'I doubt it,' she said with an assurance she was far from feeling. 'I always follow my impulses. I find first reactions are usually the most reliable.'

'If I followed mine right now I'd be shaking you to within an inch of your life!'

'What's stopping you?' she taunted, greatly daring.

With one lithe movement he was on his feet and had rounded the table towards her, catching her and pinioning her hands behind her back before she had time to evade him.

'Let me go!' She struggled, but his grasp on her tightened and against his hard strength she was helpless. She had tried him too far this time and she knew that she would pay the penalty for doing so.

'Still crediting me with the instincts of a gentleman, Kate?' he asked her.

'That's something I'd never do.' She lifted her head

defiantly and gazed into his eyes, which were no longer cold, but as turbulent and angry as a grey, winter sea. Strangely mesmeric, they caught and held her glance.

'You should have learnt by now not to push a man beyond the limits of his temper,' Nicholas Blake told her. 'But it appears that your education has been sadly neglected. It seems there's only one way of shutting you up.'

Sensing what his next action would be, she renewed her efforts to escape. But it was no use. She gave a startled cry of protest as he pulled her closer to him, moulding her against the muscled hardness of his body. For an instant he paused, apparently savouring her complete helplessness. Then his mouth came down on hers with punishing intensity, cruel and utterly ruthless in its plundering, as he forced open her lips and probed the moist sweetness beyond with leisured expertise.

As his mouth possessed hers she was conscious of a sudden primitive stirring of desire, an instinctive female response to the demands of a male. The fiery touch of his lips on hers roused her to a pitch she had never known before. She was hazily aware that this man was a past expert in the techniques of lovemaking. But this was no lover's kiss, given and returned in tenderness. It was a practised assault on her senses, intended deliberately to reduce her to absolute submission to his will.

And it was succeeding. She could feel herself weakening and the fight going out of her. Her heightened perceptions were threatening to take her over completely and an inner voice was urging her to stop battling against him and give in. Suddenly she wanted to put her arms round him and draw the taut, strong body closer to her. She wanted to return his kiss with equal intensity and show him that her desire for him was as strong as his for her.

She was fighting a losing battle, clinging desperately to the last rags of her self-control, when he released her. She took a step away from him and grasped the back of a chair for support, uncertain whether her legs would hold her up unaided.

He was breathing heavily and his lean face still bore a furious expression. He studied her for a moment in silence, then commented angrily, as if the kiss had somehow been *her* fault, 'If it gives you any satisfaction you may as well know that you're the first woman in a long time to make me lose my temper so completely. Congratulate yourself. It's quite an achievement.'

'Indeed? I can't think why,' she said sarcastically.

'Blame your own behaviour for that. I did give you fair warning.'

'My behaviour? *You* have the nerve to criticise my behaviour? It might be an idea for you to mend your own manners before you start finding fault with other people. You're absolutely primitive. Primitive as well as totally without principles!' She flung the words wildly at him, too furious to care about any possible retribution he might take.

'There's an Indian proverb to the effect that he who pulls a tiger by the tail must prepare to face his wrath. It's a valuable lesson. Perhaps you'll remember it and put a guard on that rash tongue of yours in the future.'

Instinctively she struck out at him, but he fended the blow neatly away and caught her hands in his. 'If you try that again I'll hit you back,' he cautioned her. 'You never accept that you're beaten, do you?'

Reaction was setting in and the white heat of anger which had consumed her was replaced by a curiously shaky feeling. Hot tears welled up behind her eyes and she turned her head abruptly away from him, fighting them back. She would not give him the pleasure of knowing the effect that he had wrought upon her.

'Kate?' Surely that couldn't be a note of concern in his voice? 'Are you all right?'

'No thanks to you. I hate you, Nicholas Blake!' she muttered on the verge of a sob and, with the tears she could no longer control streaming down her cheeks, she found the strength to tear herself from his grasp and run blindly for the door. It opened to admit Aunt Meg just as she reached it, but Kate brushed straight past her and into the hall beyond. Her aunt's puzzled cry followed her, but she did not stop. As she headed up the stairs she heard Nicholas Blake's voice raised in some kind of explanation without registering what he said. Let him come up with some plausible reason for upsetting her! She reached the sanctuary of her bedroom and shut and locked the door behind her. For a moment she leant against it, breathing heavily. Was anyone coming after her? No, Aunt Meg must have decided against coming to find out what was wrong. At last the pent-up emotions of the past week mingled with reaction to the scene in which she had just taken part overcame her and she stopped fighting them. Flinging herself down on the bed, she wept without restraint.

No one disturbed her and it was some two hours later, when, lying in a crumpled heap, her damp handkerchief clutched in her hand, she finally roused herself at the sound of voices in the garden below. Unsteadily she got to her feet and went over to the window to peer out. Directly beneath her she could see Aunt Meg, accompanied by the tall, unmistakable figure of Nicholas Blake. He was carrying his bags to a small, obviously hired, car which was parked in the lane beside the house. He deposited the luggage in the boot, slammed it shut and turned, smiling, to shake Aunt Meg warmly by the hand before opening the door and settling in the driving seat.

As he got into the car he turned and glanced quickly back towards the house and, although Kate was sure that the folds of the heavy curtain hid her from his view, she jumped back automatically from the window. The conceit of the man! Did he expect her to wave him on his way as if nothing had happened between them?

The engine started up and she heard her aunt shout 'Goodbye' and return to the house. So he was gone at last. She heaved a heartfelt sigh of relief. The last twenty-four hours seemed to have endured for a lifetime. The easing of tension that she felt at his departure was almost physical, a sudden lifting of the depression that had gripped her. Instantly she was brighter and ready to face the world again. Ruefully she studied her reflection in the mirror of the dressing-table and pulled a face at herself. Her hair was an untidy tangle framing features blotched by tearstains and eyes that were red and puffy from crying. What a wreck she looked! Cautiously she unlocked the door and tiptoed to the bathroom to wash.

Ten minutes later, looking considerably better, if still rather red-eyed, she made her way downstairs. What on earth could she say to Aunt Meg by way of explanation for her behaviour? That she had had a stand-up row with Nicholas Blake and, furious that he had got the better of her, had retreated to her room to indulge in a childish tantrum? That was the truth, she supposed, but there must be a better way of explaining matters.

But when she found Aunt Meg in the kitchen and began a stumbling explanation of her strange behaviour, it seemed that it was unnecessary. Nicholas Blake, with typical arrogant control of the situation, had made her excuses for her.

'I wanted to come up and see if there was anything I could do to help,' her aunt told her, 'but Mr Blake was most insistent that you needed complete rest by yourself. A friend of his has these blinding migraines, apparently, so he knew exactly what we ought to do. He said the attacks come very suddenly and often take a few hours to pass. Are you feeling better now?'

'Lots better, thank you,' Kate assured her, feeling nothing but a total fraud.

'I never knew you suffered from that sort of thing, dear. You used to be so healthy as a child. You must have been working too hard. They say stress brings these things on.'

'That's true,' she agreed. The strain of attempting to outmanoeuvre Nicholas Blake was enough to try the most placid of persons, and she readily conceded that she was hardly that.

'You must have a good rest while you're staying here,' her aunt was saying firmly. 'We can't have you going back to work in this condition.' She changed to another tack. 'Mr Blake was so charming, wasn't he? Such a pity you've missed saying goodbye to him. He was most concerned about you.'

I'll bet, thought Kate cynically, but forced a polite response. 'Are all your summer visitors like him?' she asked in an attempt to divert her aunt, and succeeded. Much to her relief Aunt Meg dismissed her most recent visitor from her mind and launched into a seemingly endless flow of horror stories about the antics of her guests over the years.

If only Kate could have forgotten him with equal ease! But it was not the case. His dark, arrogant features seemed indelibly stamped on her memory and haunted her dreams. It was a long time before she could contemplate her humiliation at his hands with anything remotely approaching composure. Yet as the days passed his image faded slightly, if not completely banished.

Surprisingly the holiday, filled with nothing more exciting than housework, shopping, visits to Aunt Meg's friends in the village and long, brisk walks through the bare winter countryside, slipped by quickly. Kate, who for all her fine words to the contrary had wondered what on earth she would find to do besides brooding about Jeremy, discovered that she had hardly any time to think about her shattered love life. The busy yet still leisured pace of village life suited her far more than the frantic bustle to which she was accustomed.

But after a fortnight she decided, despite her aunt's protests, that it was time that she got back to London and started job-hunting.

'It's been a lovely break,' she said, when Aunt Meg pressed her to stay a while longer. 'But I'm a working girl with a living to earn. Or at least, I hope to be by this time next week,' she added laughingly.

'Well, if you must go, you must and I won't try to stop you. But promise me you won't leave it so long before you visit me again.'

'Try and keep me away from your home cooking!' Kate smiled.

'And take care not to overdo it when you're back in London,' her aunt cautioned her. 'I know what it's like when you're working hard all day and then going out dancing half the night. Just remember to take it easy.'

And Kate, who had neither a job nor an attentive boy-friend waiting for her in London, smiled and meekly agreed to take care.

CHAPTER FOUR

AFTER an anxious fortnight of job-hunting Aunt Meg's parting warning about not working too hard seemed to have an almost prophetic ring to it. Kate answered advertisements and tried office staff agencies, but, although everyone assured her that trained secretaries were in the happy position of picking and choosing both where they wanted to work and what price they put on their skills, she had not been successful in obtaining even an offer of a job, let alone one which she thought would be ideal for her.

It was not that she had any difficulty in getting to the interview stage. Most would-be employers seemed only too eager for the chance to see someone of her qualifications. Her air of quiet competence coupled with a not unattractive appearance made a further good impression. But, when she explained that she had already left her last job and that it would not be convenient for them to take up references from her former employer, their enthusiasm suddenly waned.

'At the last place I went to the girl who was leaving even had the cheek to lecture me about the need for her replacement to be completely trustworthy,' Kate complained resentfully to Jane. 'When I tell them I can't give them a reference from my last job I'm finished as far as they're concerned. It's almost as if they thought I'd left because I'd been caught with my hand in the till or something.'

'Well, why won't you let them ask Jeremy for a reference?'

'You must be joking!' Kate looked appalled. 'I've got my pride, you know.'

'And that's all you've got at the moment,' her friend told her firmly. 'You're a fool to worry about Jeremy. He'd write the best reference he could dream up to get you off his back. If he thought that there was the remotest chance of you turning up to embarrass him in front of his wife and everyone at the office who must have been gossiping like mad about why you left so suddenly he'd tell any amount of lies to get you another job.'

'Thanks very much! I wasn't that bad as a secretary, you know.'

'No, of course not.' Jane floundered for a moment, wondering if she had upset her friend. 'I meant that—well, that——'

Kate laughed at the comical expression of dismay on her flat-mate's face and put her out of her misery. 'Idiot! It's all right. I know what you mean. I did make matters very easy for him and I suppose he does owe me something, if you like to see it that way. But I'm still not going to ask Jeremy for any help in getting another job. I don't want to have any contact with him or with Edwards Engineering ever again.'

'You don't have to go to see him. Just write to him,' Jane said persuasively.

'Nothing doing. Don't worry, I'll find something yet. Now, what have we got for supper tonight?' Kate changed the subject firmly and her friend, aware that she could say nothing that would make her alter her decision, wisely dropped the argument and set about inspecting the refrigerator in search of something for their evening meal.

'Omelette again, if that's all right with you?' She frowned. 'Oh dear, it's been eggs every night this week, hasn't it? I'll start clucking soon. Oh, for a nice, juicy steak or the money to buy one!'

'I'll get a job as soon as I can and then I'll be able to give my proper share of the housekeeping again.'

'For heaven's sake, Kate, I didn't mean that. A fine friend I'd be if I nagged you to get a job just to support my spare tire! I'm sorry I even mentioned it. We'll live on egg and chips for as long as it takes.'

'Sorry,' said Kate. 'I'm a bit jumpy tonight. Today I began to wonder for the first time if I'll ever find something. You've only got to switch on the radio or look at the newspaper to find about the trouble school-leavers are having when they look for work.'

'You're not a school-leaver,' Jane told her bracingly. 'You're a highly efficient, top-rank secretary. The *crème de la crème*, in fact. So stop worrying about it. It won't help matters. This time next week you'll have a super boss to work for and a salary that's out of this world and you'll be wondering why you made so much fuss.'

'Yes, you're right.' With an effort Kate smiled and, putting her cares firmly aside, managed, at least for the rest of the evening, to give an impression of buoyant optimism which fooled Jane into thinking that her words had had some effect.

They had, but not the one for which she had hoped. As she lay tossing and sleepless in bed that night Kate's thoughts chased each other round in circles, endlessly considering new avenues which she might search for a job. Jane had been kind to her, too generous in refusing to take Kate's share of the housekeeping until she found something she really liked. But her pride revolted at the prospect of living off Jane any longer. Yet, as Jane herself had pointed out, it was that very pride that was blocking her way at the moment. Perhaps her friend was right and she should approach Jeremy and ask for his help. No! Anything would be better than that.

Then the solution struck her with blinding suddenness. She recalled, as if she had just spoken the words, her defiant reply to Nicholas Blake when he had told, or rather commanded, her to get in touch with him if she needed a job. She had flung the offer in his face. 'I'd rather starve in the street than work for you,' she had answered him. She smiled bitterly. The prospect was less of a laughing matter now than it had been when she had tossed the words defiantly at him. She could remember how his strong features had tautened as he had fought to control his anger. Her face burned at the memory. How could she have been so rude to him?

Could she now approach him as if nothing had happened between them and ask him for a job? Every instinct cried out at the idea of crawling to him and humbling herself by begging him for work. For he would glory in the prospect, she was sure. But there was the remote possibility that he might help her. She got out of bed, flung on her dressing-gown and went to the living room to find the telephone directory. There was no harm in looking up his number, after all . . .

Two days later, after a particularly unpleasant afternoon with a potential employer whose roving eyes took more interest in her legs than in her typing speeds, she decided that there was nothing to be lost by ringing Nicholas Blake. She had reached bottom, too dispirited to care very much what his reaction might be. Yet, strangely, her fingers trembled slightly as she dialled the number of his office. As she waited for someone to answer she nearly put the phone down again.

Perhaps Nicholas Blake would be away, out of the office or just too busy to bother with a troublesome female he had encountered over a month ago. He had probably forgotten all about her. With these encouraging thoughts she asked the switchboard to put her through to him. At least she would have tried.

'Yes?' There was no mistaking that brusque note of authority. Nicholas Blake was a man who wasted no time on social niceties, as Kate knew to her cost. She stumbled, the opening sentences of the explanation she had rehearsed for his secretary's benefit instantly deserting her.

'It's Kate Sherwood, Mr Blake. You—you may not remember me, but we met about——'

He cut in impatiently. 'How could I forget someone of your undoubted talents? What can I do for you?'

She took a deep breath. 'I'm looking for a job, as I believe I may have mentioned when we talked last. You did say you might be able to help me ...' Her voice trailed nervously away.

'I'm sure you'll correct me if I'm wrong, but I seem to remember also that you spurned my offer with every appearance of loathing.'

He was going to make it difficult for her. Should she give up now or plough on in the hope that matters might improve? She had nothing to lose. 'I'm sorry,' she said stiffly. The words stuck in her throat. 'That was stupid of me. And rather childish.'

'Yes, it was, wasn't it?' he taunted her. 'Fortunately I have a forgiving nature. Come to my office at ten o'clock tomorrow and I'll see if I can find a use for you.'

'But——' There was no answer, except the sound of the receiver being replaced at the other end. Kate glared angrily at the phone. How typical of the man to issue an order and expect instant obedience from her! Just who did he think he was? But as she went into the kitchen to make herself a cup of coffee to steady her shaking nerves after the ordeal she knew that she would keep the appointment. She had no option.

She told Jane the news when her flatmate got home from work.

'I've got another interview tomorrow. It seems quite promising.'

'Where this time?'

Kate adopted a casual tone. 'He's called Nicholas Blake. I met him when I was staying with Aunt Meg.' She had not mentioned the encounter to her friend before, being only too keen to put the thought of her shame to the back of her mind. 'He told me to get in touch with him if I ever needed a job, but I'd forgotten all about him until now.'

'Not Nicholas Blake the financial wizard?'

'He does have an office in the City, yes.'

Jane was staring at her open-mouthed. 'You *forgot* about meeting Nicholas Blake? Are you sickening for something?'

'You've heard of him, then?' Kate asked, puzzled. The name had seemed familiar when she had first heard it, but she had failed to make any connection.

'Who hasn't unless they've been in Outer Mongolia for the last few years? Do you live in a dream world, Kate? You ought to study the papers a little more carefully. He's only one of the most successful financiers in the business world. He started operations ten years ago with nothing but his wits to help him, and now he's made it big. He must be practically a millionaire.'

'Since when have you looked at the City pages?' Kate teased, nonetheless impressed by the knowledge.

Jane grinned happily. 'You know that I don't. But I do read the gossip columns, and Nicholas Blake features pretty heavily in those from time to time. And you met him and never even told me! Honestly, Kate, if you didn't recognise the name how could you forget such a gorgeous hunk of man? He'd make an impact on any female. I've seen his photograph often enough to know that.'

'Yes, I suppose he was quite attractive,' Kate allowed.

'Quite attractive! What's wrong with you? He's absolutely devastating. And if the gossip columns are anything to go by, I'm not the only one who thinks so. He's always knee-deep in beautiful women trying to get their hands on him. That combination of looks and brains is dynamite.'

'Not for me, it wasn't,' Kate said calmly. 'Oh, he was handsome enough, I'll grant you that, but——'

'But nothing compared with your Jeremy, I suppose. When are you going to get that man out of your mind? You must be absolutely mad to let a man like Nicholas Blake slip out of your clutches.' Jane was nothing if not an opportunist. 'They say he has a different woman every week. Did he make a pass at you?'

'Certainly not!' Kate could feel her colour rising. 'Well,' she qualified, 'he did kiss me, but that was only because he was furious with me.'

'He kissed you! Sit down this instant and tell me everything,' her friend commanded. 'You're not stirring from this room until I've heard the full story.'

So Kate told her the tale of her encounter with Nicholas Blake and how they had parted. 'We didn't exactly leave each other on the friendliest of terms,' she concluded. 'He was absolutely beside himself with anger. I don't think anyone had dared to tell him any home truths about himself before. But I didn't care. I assumed that I'd never see him again.'

'But he must have forgiven you if he's agreed to see you and talk about finding you a job?'

'He's the most unforgiving character I've ever met,' Kate said ruefully. 'He probably just wants to have the pleasure of seeing me crawl to him in person.'

'And are you going to?' Jane asked.

'No. I'm not scared of Nicholas Blake!'

But even as she uttered the bold words Kate felt a tremor of apprehension go down her spine.

The next day she dressed with care for the appointment. After standing in front of her wardrobe for a good half hour debating what to wear, she had finally chosen what Jeremy had referred to as her 'schoolmarm' outfit, a classic, camel-coloured suit, cut on severe lines, which had always given her slender figure an air of authority. The skirt was perhaps a few inches too short to be fashionable by this year's standards, but, teamed with a toning wool sweater, it complemented her colouring admirably and made her feel quietly confident. She applied a light make-up, brushed her hair, pulling it into the neat chignon in which she usually wore it for work, and studied her reflection in the mirror.

If appearances counted for anything she was the perfect secretary and certainly looked cool and confident enough in the role to erase Nicholas Blake's initial disastrous impression of her. If only her inner self could be as calm and controlled as her outer one suggested! Instead she was a jangling mass of nerves and uncertainties. She stuck out her tongue at the prim reflection and set out to meet the man she had once thought she would be glad never to see again.

The building in the heart of the City where Nicholas Blake had his offices was modern, an aggressive mass of steel and plate glass which towered high above the grimier buildings which surrounded it. Inside, however, the reception area was attractively designed and welcoming with thick piled carpets and a number of comfortable easy chairs. Kate gave her name to the girl at the reception desk and sat down to await her summons to

Nicholas Blake. Outwardly a picture of composed confidence, she could feel her courage ebbing away with every passing second.

But it was too late to retreat now. A pleasant blonde girl was approaching her with a smile. This must be his secretary.

'Miss Sherwood? I'm Sarah Wilkins—I work as Mr Blake's personal assistant. Will you come this way, please?'

So this was the poor girl he had shouted at over the phone. Kate studied her as the other girl led the way through a maze of corridors and turnings. She certainly did not seem unduly crushed and downtrodden. Perhaps, working with a man like Nicholas Blake, one developed a resilience which helped one to cope with the man.

'It's a bit of a rabbit warren, I know, but you'll soon get used to it. After a week or so you learn your way around.'

That sounded hopeful, Kate thought. Had he perhaps mentioned the post he had in mind to his assistant? There was no chance to find out, however, for her companion halted suddenly in front of a door to their left, knocked, and opened it.

'Miss Sherwood to see you,' she announced, and stood aside, indicating that Kate should enter.

She felt as if her only ally in this confusing place had deserted her as she took a step forward and heard the door close behind her. Suddenly she felt more alone and unsure of herself than ever before. She had no time for more than a quick glance around her and gained a vague impression of a large room, elegantly but sparsely furnished in a style that was contemporary, but pleasantly so. A couple of bright modern paintings hung on one wall, while another was completely taken up by a vast picture window which gave a dizzying, panoramic view out over the sprawling mass that was London. To one side of the window was a heavy, leather-topped desk, piled high with an untidy confusion of papers. But it did not dominate the room. *That* was the prerogative of the man who sat behind it, his keen grey glance scrutinising every inch of her as she walked from the door and came to a self-conscious halt before him.

She did not know why she expected him to have changed. Perhaps it was because the Nicholas Blake who had haunted her dreams after her last encounter with him had become a demon of almost outsize proportions, terrifying her with the way he rode roughshod over her feelings and ignored her frightened protests. Today he appeared the proper businessman, immaculate in a sombre, well-cut suit, with a crisp white shirt which emphasised the strong column of his throat and the clean, firm line of his jaw. The springy dark hair, brushed severely away from his forehead; the piercing grey eyes, whose variations of tone mirrored his changing moods; the firm but sensual lips, which knew the secret of how to rouse a woman both to passion and to fury; all added up to a picture of a dangerously good-looking man. A man who would count his charm and appeal for women as marketable assets and who would use them to win every trick.

It seemed he had little time to waste on Kate. Glancing at his watch, he motioned her to a chair and asked briskly, 'Sit down, Miss Sherwood, and tell me how I can help you.' The voice was as she remembered, cool and completely impersonal. She might have been a block of wood as far as he was concerned. If the circumstances of their last meeting were in his mind, he gave no indication of it.

She complied, perching uneasily on the edge of the seat by his desk. From any other employer the words might have sounded hopeful. Coming from him they merely increased her unease. He knew as well as she did why she was here. She raised her chin in an unconscious gesture of challenge and launched straight into a request for a job, giving him a brief outline of her qualifications and the previous posts she had held.

He heard her out, then asked abruptly, 'How do you cope under presure?'

'I'm used to hard work, Mr Blake. I'm not afraid of it.'

'And working to a deadline?'

'It doesn't worry me. It takes an exceptional set of circumstances to throw me off balance.'

'Indeed?' His tone was faintly mocking. 'I'm flattered you think so.'

She had walked into that trap with her eyes open. Damn the man! 'I was talking about my office work,' she said stiffly.

'Yes, of course, Miss Sherwood.' The mockery was still there. 'You've got adequate typing and shorthand, I suppose?'

'Yes, I——'

He raised an impatient hand. 'Spare me the details. I'll decide for myself whether you're as good as you claim to be. Here's paper.' He tossed a pad across the desk to her. 'Take a letter, will you?' Barely waiting for her to find a pen from her handbag, he spoke rapidly, dictating an account of a complicated business deal for a fellow financier and making no allowances for her nervousness or possible lack of knowledge of some of the technical terms he used. He set a punishing pace, but Kate, aware that he was doing it deliberately, had no intention of asking him to slow down. It was a struggle to keep up, but somehow she managed it.

He came to a sudden halt. 'Now read it back,' he demanded, and she did so, stumbling slightly over the occasional unfamiliar word. He cut her short before she had gone further than the first paragraph. 'Right. You'll do.'

'You mean you can find me a job?' The relief from tension made her feel almost faint.

'If that's what you want.'

'But you don't know what my typing's like,' she protested weakly. 'And then there's the question of references from my previous employer.'

He shrugged. 'I assume your typing is up to standard or you'd hardly be wasting my time. As to references, I'd prefer to trust to my own judgment of character rather than that of other people.'

'And what is your judgment of my character?' she asked, greatly daring.

He took his time in answering her, his grey eyes studying her with almost insulting slowness. 'Basically sound, if a little impetuous when someone knocks you off your guard.' He looked at his watch again and frowned. 'Now I have work to do, if you'll excuse me. I assume you'll be free to start work on Monday? Good. My secretary will fill you in on the other relevant details and answer any questions you may have.'

'Yes, of course.' Kate smiled her thanks. It had not been as bad as she had expected after all. 'That's wonderful news. I'm very grateful to you for giving me a chance. I hope you won't have cause to regret it.'

There was a curious expression in his eyes. 'So do I, Miss Sherwood.'

She gathered up her handbag and prepared to go.

'Haven't you forgotten something?' he asked abruptly.

She looked at him enquiringly, then realised. 'You

mean the salary you're offering?' She smiled. 'You must think me very unworldly. I assumed your secretary would mention that.'

He named a sum far in excess of what she had received at Edwards Engineering and brushed aside her stunned cry of protest. 'Don't worry, I'm not overpaying you. You'll earn every penny of it, I assure you.'

She turned to go. His voice halted her in her tracks. Silky smooth, it held a warning note, although she could not imagine why.

'You don't seem too curious about the hard taskmaster for whom you'll be working.'

Kate laughed. 'How foolish of me! Will your secretary introduce me to him now or do I wait until Monday to see him?' Her face fell as another thought struck her. 'Perhaps he'll want to decide for himself if we can work together successfully before you confirm my appointment.'

'And you, very naturally, will want to make sure that your new boss is not—what was the expression you used—high-handed and impossible?'

Sarcastic beast, she thought viciously, but controlled herself and responded sweetly, 'I find I can get on with most people if I try hard enough, Mr Blake. For the salary you're offering I'd work for the devil himself.'

'Indeed? In that case I think you'll find we'll deal quite well together.'

A sudden feeling of horror gripped her at his words. 'You don't mean that I—that you——'

His smile was faintly malicious. 'I mean that Miss Wilkins, after four traumatic months in my employment, is leaving me to get married and I need a replacement for her.' He sounded suddenly impatient. 'That's the only vacancy I can offer you at the moment. Take it or leave it.'

Kate's thoughts were in a turmoil. Never in her wildest nightmares had she dreamt that she might end up working as Nicholas Blake's personal secretary. Her stunned face must have reflected her emotions accurately, but he gave her no time to recover from the shock he had sprung on her.

'Struck dumb for once, Kate?' he taunted her. 'Or are you trying to phrase a tactful refusal?'

She was silent, her brain reeling frantically in an effort to take in the sudden revelation.

'Perhaps you don't feel capable of dealing with the pressures the work might hold?' he continued, his voice dark with mockery. 'It's a very demanding post and requires a fair amount of initiative. I'm away a good deal and I'd expect you to take charge. I'm sorry if you feel it wouldn't suit you, but I'll understand, of course.'

And forgive her, no doubt, for wasting his valuable time in the bargain. How dared he suggest that she could not cope? Kate threw caution to the winds and with it her first blind instinct to turn down his offer with a few polite words and leave his office as fast as her legs could carry her. 'Not at all,' she heard herself respond coolly. 'I always enjoy a challenge.'

'So it would seem. I'll try not to disappoint you.' His expression was impossible to read, but she had the curious impression that he was feeling triumph rather than chagrin at her sudden enthusiastic acceptance of the job. Heaven alone knew why he had offered the post to her of all people. There would be a queue a mile long if he advertised for a secretary.

Almost as if he had read the question in her mind he continued calmly, 'Naturally you're puzzled as to why I should avail myself of your services when I could choose almost anyone?'

Kate bit back the tart reply that hovered on her tongue.

'Let's just say I didn't think you held a very high opinion of my talents on the strength of our meetings so far,' she said. That was his fault entirely, but she refrained from stating the obvious.

'Not at all.' In one lithe movement he got to his feet and walked round the desk towards her. Without its comforting bulk between them Kate felt strangely insecure, uncertain of what his next move might be. 'You underestimate yourself, Kate. As far as I'm concerned your secretarial speeds, excellent though they may be, come a poor second to the one outstanding qualification I'm well aware you do possess.'

What game was he playing now? She shifted a little uneasily in her chair, intensely aware of him in front of her. He was only inches away from her and she found the powerful figure unnerving in its closeness to her, although she could not have said why. 'Oh?' she enquired warily. 'You grant me one virtue at least, then. I suppose I should be grateful.'

'Aren't you curious to know exactly what that virtue is?' He leaned back, resting casually against the desk, relaxed and completely in command of the situation. He was enjoying baiting her, she was sure of that.

She shrugged, feigning indifference. 'Well?'

'I expect a certain standard of efficiency and, make no mistake, you'll earn your place in my office or you'll be out so fast that you won't know what's hit you. But one thing I won't tolerate is some little fool mooning over me and wasting time by making me the object of her romantic fantasies. It's caused problems in the past.' The grey eyes raked her dispassionately. 'If I've judged you correctly you won't make that mistake.'

The conceit of the man! Did he imagine that a woman had only to look at him and the admittedly attractive picture he presented to fall head over heels in love with him? 'I think I can set your mind at rest on that point,' she told him decisively. 'I hardly imagine I'm likely to become besotted with you. In fact I'm sure I'm immune to your charms, such as they are.'

The insult, if he registered it at all, passed him by. 'You're to be congratulated.'

'For my discernment?' she fenced coolly, pretending a calm she was far from feeling.

'Let's say for your good sense.' There was a hint of devilry in the smile that he slanted at her. 'Although, if it weren't for the havoc it would wreak with the office routine, I might be almost tempted to see what it was like to break down those defences of yours. It could be quite an enjoyable experience.'

'For you or me?'

'Possibly for both of us.'

'You'd fail, *Mr* Blake. Office romances don't interest me.'

'There's always a first time.'

'Yes, but never a second,' she countered quickly.

'I see. Once bitten, twice shy?' He sounded faintly intrigued.

She got hastily to her feet. 'If that's all I won't take up any more of your time. I believe you said you had work to do. I think your present secretary can put me right about everything else I want to know.' She held out her hand in a gesture of farewell.

'Including how to handle the boss?' The lean, hard fingers closed round hers and retained them in a firm grasp.

'I don't think I need advice on that.'

'You sound very confident.'

'Shouldn't I be?' The touch of his hand on hers was

sending strange, thrilling vibrations through her and it was an effort to resist the impulse to tear away from his hold.

'You may find me rather different from your former employer,' he told her. 'I'd hate to think you'd bitten off more than you could chew.'

'I'm sure there's no danger of that.'

'We'll see, shall we?' He released her hand abruptly. 'I shall be most interested to find out.'

In spite of her coolness in the face of Nicholas Blake's onslaught it was with considerable trepidation that Kate faced her first day in her new job. Sarah, his outgoing secretary, who seemed to regard him with an equal mixture of affection and dread, did much to smooth the way by explaining the office routine and Kate was relieved to find that, although taxing, the job was clearly well within her capabilities. Whether she could deal with her new employer with the same confidence she was considerably less positive.

She trod warily, only too conscious that this was the same man who had meted out such shattering punishment to her when they had clashed before. If he was piqued in any way by the cool indifference which, by a great effort on her part, coloured Kate's dealings with him, he gave no indication of it. His manner towards her was casual, even remote at times, and he rarely favoured her with one of the charming smiles which secured him the instant devotion of any female within range. It seemed Kate was no more to him than a reasonably useful piece of office furniture.

If he appreciated or even noticed the way she fitted in with his quick-fire decisions, anticipated his orders and coped in his frequent trips abroad, he never remarked on it, but she assumed that as far as Nicholas Blake was concerned only failure merited remark. Although logic told her to be grateful that he had not followed up his threat of making her change her opinion of him, her feminine pride resented his cavalier attitude towards her and she had a strong suspicion that he sensed as much. Occasionally she was aware of a mocking glance in her direction, almost as if he had recognised her struggle to resist his attraction, and it amused him to watch the effort it cost her to remain aloof and detached.

The work was hard, but he demanded nothing of her that he was not prepared to ask of himself and, as the weeks flew by, she could only marvel and grudgingly admire the ruthless brain whose astounding City successes were due partly to his uncanny flair for business, but also to his seemingly inexhaustible capacity for hard work. Top level finance meetings took him across the Atlantic at a moment's notice, but on his return he would settle down to deal with the work that accumulated in his absence and a punishing schedule of overdue appointments as if he had just come back from a month's holiday.

To a woman the female staff doted on him and envied Kate her closeness to him. 'It's sickening the way they fall at his feet,' she complained to Jane. 'As if he were something special.'

'You mean he isn't?' her flat-mate teased her. 'Oh, Kate, haven't you joined the admiring throng yet?'

'No. And I'm hardly likely to.'

'You still care about Jeremy? I hoped you'd put that business behind you.'

'I have.' It was impossible to explain that however much she succeeded in plunging resolutely into work and trying to forget Jeremy, it would be a long time before the shock of his betrayal faded.

'Then why are you closing your eyes to a golden opportunity? Nicholas Blake must be worth a mint. And I bet he knows how to give a girl a good time.' Jane's voice was wistful. 'Dinners in the best restaurants in town, nightclubs, parties—you could have a ball. It beats egg and chips in the local Wimpy any day. Give it a whirl. You've nothing to lose.'

Kate laughed and shook her head. 'I've everything to lose. He doesn't like his secretaries falling for him. I like my job, thank you very much. I might be a fly on the wall for all the notice he takes of me as a woman, and I'd sooner keep it that way. Besides, who cares about high living if it's with a man you can't stand? I'd rather have beans on toast with someone I really liked.'

'The lady doth protest too much, methinks,' her friend commented sourly. 'An escort like Nicholas Blake would soon know how to change your mind. Anyway, I don't know how you can work with him every day and still pretend you dislike him.'

'Quite easily, I assure you,' Kate lied firmly. 'Oh, he's attractive, but——'

'Attractive? He's every girl's dream!'

'Not mine.'

Jane ignored her. 'Sophisticated, good-looking, rich, intelligent——'

'Arrogant, strong-willed, ruthless, dictatorial,' Kate completed the list.

'All right, I give in.' Jane raised her hands in mock surrender. 'If you can't recognise a gorgeous man when he's right in front of your nose, there's no hope for you. Does *he* know what you think of him?'

Kate's mind flew back to the occasion when she had told him exactly what she had thought of him and the memory of his response was all too vivid. 'I imagine so,' she said casually. 'Why?'

'I just hope he never takes it into his head to try to

alter your opinion. I know who I'd back to win that particular contest.'

'You'd be wrong.'

'Would I? Don't be too sure. From what I hear he's not the sort of man who fails to get what he wants, whether it's a business deal or a woman.'

'In that case,' Kate told her friend lightly, 'it's just as well he doesn't want me. I'd hate you to witness his first failure.'

CHAPTER FIVE

WITH her friend's words fresh in her mind Kate found herself studying her employer closely the next day as she sat, pencil poised, waiting for Nicholas to digest the details of a foreign query and dictate an answer to it. Yes, Jane was right, she conceded reluctantly, as she took in every inch of the lithe, immaculately suited figure. Nicholas Blake was all imperious male, she decided, scanning the handsome features which were saved from the insipidity of mere good looks by the firm chin and broad, intelligent forehead. Even now, as he sat puzzling over the letter in his hand and utterly unconscious of the appearance he presented, there was a magnetism about him, a virile attraction which even she felt, dislike him as she might.

What would it be like, she wondered, to have him as the man in one's life, an attentive, stimulating partner, dancing attendance and humouring one's every whim? As quickly as the thought came she rejected it. Any woman in his life would fit in with his wishes and play the subordinate role. And, if the gossip columns, as relayed by Jane, were to be believed, any number of glamorous women were prepared to do just that. The prospect of snaring the man the newspapers had christened 'the City's most eligible bachelor' must be almost irresistible.

The latest in a long line of fashionable beauties appeared to be Diana Kendall, the socialite daughter of a wealthy businessman, a girl who, as far as Kate could discover, combined amazing good looks with the bare minimum of brains. But perhaps he preferred that blend. No doubt it saved arguments. He had been visiting the Kendalls' country estate and had been dashing back to London when he had come upon Kate in the middle of his path. A peep in his diary had established that fact, although she had felt almost guilty at the curiosity which had prompted her to look for the information. As if his personal life was any concern of hers. A smile crossed her face at the thought of the contrast between the elegance of Diana Kendall's exquisitely groomed face and figure and her own appearance that night in her aunt's old dressing gown. Nicholas Blake had certainly gone from the sublime to the ridiculous that night!

'If you're quite ready?' A coldly sarcastic tone penetrated her thoughts.

She jumped in confusion at the sound. 'Sorry. I was miles away.'

'So it would appear.' He thrust the letter aside and turned his concentrated gaze on her, the grey eyes uncomfortably penetrating. 'Whatever it was seemed to be causing you some amusement. Perhaps you'd like to share the joke with me?'

She fenced desperately. 'I don't think you'd find it particularly funny. It was just something private.'

He frowned impatiently. 'If it's your latest boy-friend who's occupying your mind, do you think that you could make an effort to forget him for a moment or two at least so that you can get this letter down? Or is that too much to ask?'

'No, Mr Blake.' She accepted the rebuke meekly, feeling like a schoolgirl who had been told off for talking in class. She wondered what his reaction would have been if she had told him he had been, at least indirectly, the object of her amusement. It didn't seem worth the explanation. She straightened in her chair and projected an air of eager efficiency as she waited for him to return to the letter by his hand.

But he seemed in no hurry to do so. 'I expected better of you than this. You've made quite a promising start and I'll admit I've been pleasantly surprised by the way you've managed to grasp the essentials in the short time you've been working here. But if you're going to let your private life start interfering with your work, you're hardly likely to stay the course with me. What you do after five o'clock is your own affair and I don't give a damn. But I expect your complete co-operation during office hours, and that means one hundred per cent, not any less. Is that clear?'

'Perfectly. I think you've made your point,' Kate said tightly, suppressing the angry retort that had risen instinctively to her lips. Patronising, dictatorial man! Did he really think that she was that stupid? Obviously he did. She supposed it was partly her fault for daydreaming. But to dress her down like a junior typist in her first week at work was uncalled for. 'It won't happen again,' she told him firmly.

'I trust not. Now let's get on.'

After that there was no time for her attention to wander as she took down the letters he dictated fast and furiously for the rest of the morning. She escaped from his room at last, flexing her cramped fingers as she collapsed in her own chair. He wanted this batch of letters completed for signature before she left the office and she resigned herself to working through her lunch hour to make sure that she had them ready in time. This of all days was not one for excuses for unfinished tasks! With sandwiches and a cup of coffee by her typewriter she set to work.

For once her usual speed and accuracy deserted her and she made error after error. The coffee grew cold and the sandwiches curled unattractively as she ploughed on, her wastepaper basket filling steadily with rejected sheets of paper. Drat the man for knocking her off balance! One minor outburst from him, she thought, and she spent the rest of the day demonstrating the sort of incompetence which he so clearly expected from her. Sighing, she put yet another sheet of paper in the typewriter and tried again.

This time things went a little better and the pile was half completed when the door of her office opened. She looked up impatiently, ready to get rid of the unwelcome intruder as quickly as politeness would allow.

The vision that entered the room and bathed it in a cloud of Chanel Number 5 took Kate's breath away. If Diana Kendall's face looked beautiful in the blurred reproductions of the daily papers, the reality was even more stunning. The mane of titian hair which fell to her shoulders in a carefully arranged disorder made a glorious frame for her exquisite face. The black dress she wore displayed far too much cleavage for that time of day, but it enhanced her porcelain complexion and displayed her spectacular figure to perfection, and she knew it. A pair of carefully made up green eyes flashed a winning smile at Kate as their owner headed for the inner office which Nicholas Blake occupied.

Kate sprang hastily to her feet. 'Have you an appointment with Mr Blake?'

The other girl halted and turned a blank face towards her. 'You're Nicky's new secretary, are you, darling?' She giggled. 'The dragon who scares everybody away from him. No, I haven't got an appointment, but he'll see me.' She smiled confidently. 'I'm his fiancée.'

She would call him Nicky in that affected way. Kate wondered how he responded to the endearment. But however close Diana was to him in private life, she could not see him welcoming an interruption in whatever attractive guise at this particular moment. He had lunched on sandwiches which he had ordered to be served in his room and he had given strict instructions that he was not to be disturbed as he worked on the details of a complicated deal he was setting up for an important client. Kate planted herself firmly in front of the door leading to the inner office and, feeling rather like Horatius defending the bridge, attempted diplomatically to restrain the other girl.

'I'm not sure whether Mr Blake is free just now. He's a very busy man, you know,' she improvised swiftly. 'Perhaps if you came back a little later? I'm sure you must have some shopping to do.'

'I want to see Nicky now,' Diana pouted, looking for all the world like a child about to be deprived of a favourite toy. 'I'll see him when *I* want to. How dare you try to keep me out!' Her voice rose shrilly as she tried to sidestep Kate and reach the inner sanctum. 'Get out of my way!'

'Miss Kendall, please——' Kate's voice rose too in an effort to make the other girl see reason.

The door in front of which they were arguing opened with a sudden crash and Nicholas Blake stood there, the expression on his face boding ill for someone.

'I can't hear myself think for noise. What the hell is going on?' he demanded. 'Miss Sherwood?'

He would pick on her for an explanation, she thought resentfully. Before she had time to attempt an excuse Diana had rushed forward and flung her arms around him.

'Nicky! Darling! It's your stupid secretary. She wanted to fend me off by telling me you were too busy to see me.' She smiled engagingly up at him, the green eyes innocent and adoring. 'As if you'd ever be too busy to see me!

You're not angry with me, are you, Nicky darling?'

His bad temper apparently forgotten, he smiled indulgently at her. 'Of course I'm not angry with you.'

Kittenlike she draped herself round his arm and darted a hostile look at Kate who was standing, lost for words at her employer's sudden change of mood. 'You must tell her not to do it again,' Diana demanded. 'And make her apologise to me for treating me like any old visitor.'

'You'll have to forgive her, Diana. Miss Sherwood has a lot to learn,' he said drily. The grim expression in his eyes promised retribution at some not too distant date. 'Perhaps you could manage to produce some coffee for us?' he asked rather wearily. 'I don't know about Diana, but *I* could certainly use some.'

'Oh, poor Nicky, you've been working too hard again.' The soft, rather babyish voice offered sympathy as he led Diana tenderly into his office and the door closed behind them.

When Kate took in the tray of coffee a few minutes later it was obvious that she had chosen the wrong moment. Diana, her arms drawing Nicholas lovingly close to her and her mouth pressed hungrily to his, gave no sign that she was aware of a sudden third party breaking up the tête-à-tête. She made a little moue of protest as he put her firmly aside, wiping traces of her lipstick from his face without any sign of embarrassment. Kate put the tray on his desk and made her escape with a burning face.

It was another half hour before the door opened and Nicholas ushered Diana Kendall out of his room and bade her a fond farewell before despatching her on her way. As he strode back to his office he called impatiently over his shoulder for Kate to join him.

The dark fury that she saw in his face unleashed itself on her the moment she entered the room. 'What the hell do you mean by letting Diana descend on me?'

'I could hardly bar the door to her,' she snapped back at him. 'Or do you think I should have let her trample all over me in her determination to get to your room?'

'I expected you to use a little sense and to understand that when I give instructions not to let anyone bother me I mean precisely that.'

'I didn't think Miss Kendall counted as "anyone",' Kate said stiffly. 'After all, she is the girl you're going to marry.'

'Indeed?' The anger was replaced by a look of malicious amusement. 'I didn't know you took such an interest in my private life. Don't believe everything the gossip columnists put about.'

'I don't read gossip columns,' she retorted. 'Miss Kendall told me herself that she was your fiancée.'

'And you believed her?' He gave a short, incredulous laugh. 'Can you see me marrying Diana?' he demanded.

'Who you decide to marry is nothing to do with me.'

'Always the discreet little secretary,' he taunted. 'Don't tell me you haven't had thoughts on the subject.'

'If I have I keep them to myself.'

'Unlike Diana, who's been telling the world—or such of it that cares to listen to her—that she'll get me to the altar.'

'And will she?' Kate could not resist putting the question.

'No.' His tone was decisive. 'She has admirable qualities—in a girl-friend—but as a wife, no.' He shrugged. 'She'll have to go.'

'You don't sound too upset about it.'

'Should I be? Knowing when to free myself of entanglements is the secret of my success.'

'Apparently,' she said tartly.

He studied her for a long moment. 'You don't like me

very much, do you?' he asked suddenly. He picked up an exquisitely carved ivory paper-knife from his desk and turned it restlessly in his hands. Against the tanned strength of his fingers its intricacy looked even more fragile, a beautiful object strangely threatened by the hidden power within him.

Kate felt cornered. 'Aren't you satisfied with my work?' she countered defensively, refusing to be drawn. Personal criticism had already got her into enough hot water with Nicholas Blake.

'Your work's well nigh perfect and you know it. I'm talking about your personal feelings.'

'I was taught never to let my personal likes and dislikes interfere with my work. They don't matter,' she said, calmly enough.

'On the contrary, they matter a good deal.' He was leaning against the desk, completely at his ease as he examined her face, his grey eyes dark with curiosity. 'Go ahead. Don't feel you have to spare my finer feelings. You disapprove of me, don't you?'

She felt suddenly reckless. For once Nicholas Blake was going to hear the truth about himself and blow the consequences. 'Yes, I do.'

'At least that's a start. I'd rather have good, honest dislike from you than the cool, indifferent face you've presented to me for the last few weeks. Why?'

'You're cold and calculating and you use people for your own advantage.'

'So? I'm a businessman, not a plaster saint. Wheeling and dealing contributes to my success. My rivals know what to expect and if they can't take the pace they can get out of the market. I think you'll find more sharp practice than I've ever stooped to among the people trying to outmanoeuvre me.' He got to his feet and paced restlessly over to the window. She was suddenly aware of the virile strength of that lean, hard-muscled figure and fought against the magnetism it exerted on her. As if conscious of the effect he had on her, he went on smoothly, 'But it's the women you're talking about, isn't it?'

She was silent.

'Isn't it, Kate?' he persisted.

'Yes,' she said, raising her head and meeting his gaze defiantly. 'If you want a straight answer, I don't approve of playboys.' It was an unfair criticism and she knew it. Nicholas Blake played hard, but he worked hard too.

'Meaning?'

'You waste a lot of time on dumb redheads.'

One dark eyebrow was raised, not in anger as she had expected, but in amusement. 'Jealous, Kate?'

'Good heavens, no.' She tried to inject the right amount of scorn into her voice. 'I wouldn't want to be one of the harem who follow you about. You seem to regard all females as simply there to gratify your pleasure *and* your vanity. They form an endless queue for your attentions and when you're tired of someone you cast her aside and take up the next in line. You change girl-friends the way most men change shirts. Does it never occur to you to think about *their* feelings for a change?'

He gave a cynical smile. 'The most attractive feature about me as far as most of them are concerned is my bank balance. No woman's ever broken her heart over me. They know the score. They have a good time when they're with me and afterwards they move on quite happily, I assure you.'

'Even Diana?'

'Diana,' he said without heat, 'is, despite of or because of her background, a hard-headed, mercenary little bitch, who isn't worth the sympathy you're lavishing on her. Despite her little-girl manner she's no fool. She's got a cash register where her heart should be and hasn't ever been able to bring herself to go out with a man unless his yearly income is over the five-figure mark. Unfortunately for her she broke the rules she set for herself and for the first time in her money-grabbing life she's overestimated her talents and decided I'm good husband material.'

'And are you?' queried Kate sceptically.

'As far as I'm concerned a husband possesses other qualities besides the ability to write limitless cheques for his wife to squander. It seems highly unlikely that I'll ever find a woman who looks beyond the sugary coating of my bank balance and loves the man underneath, faults and all, but if I do I'll review the situation. Until then——' he shrugged expressively.

'And Diana will go the way of all the others?'

'Do you care?' he asked curiously. 'I told you, she's not worth your sympathy.'

'Perhaps she's more involved than you think,' she said, thinking of the countless photographs she had seen of the two of them together, Nicholas looking his usual arrogant, slightly bored self, while Diana had gazed adoringly up at him. Was it just a pose? Kate didn't know. 'I wouldn't like to think of her getting hurt. You treat women like dirt.'

'You're too soft-hearted,' he jeered. 'Possibly she'll get slightly bruised when I decide it's time to cut loose.' He gave a slow, slightly cruel smile. 'But I'm sure she'll recover soon enough when the next attractive man comes into her sights. She'll learn her lesson and know better next time.'

'You're a callous swine!' Kate flung the words at him, careless of how he might react.

'I prefer to call myself realistic.' He stood, eyeing her thoughtfully for a moment. 'Really, Kate, are you so piqued because I haven't tried to add you to my list of conquests? That can be easily remedied.'

She came suddenly to her senses. Past experience had taught her what happened when she crossed swords with this man and she had no desire to repeat her previous humiliation at his hands. She must be out of mind to be tempting Fate like this. What secretary would ever speak to her boss the way she had just done? But what boss could be as inconsiderate and arrogant as Nicholas Blake had been? She took a deep breath to calm herself and started again, ignoring his question. 'You're still annoyed with me. I can only apologise for letting Miss Kendall disturb you. It won't happen again. If that's all, Mr Blake, I'll go and get on with some work.'

'You'll do nothing of the sort. I haven't finished with you yet.' There was a soft threat in his voice.

A warning bell clamoured somewhere inside Kate's head and she backed warily in the direction of the door. 'I've some letters to finish. You said they were urgent. I'd better——'

'They'll wait,' he said calmly with a smile that she distrusted.

She turned to flee for the safety of the outer office, but he was too quick for her and, with one swift movement, he had reached the door, turned the key in the lock and pocketed it. 'You'll stay here until I decide you can go and not before. It's not like you, Kate, to abandon an argument just as it was getting interesting.'

'Do you need to lock me in to make sure that I continue the discussion?'

'You seemed to be on the verge of taking to your heels.' There was a look of sardonic amusement in his eyes. 'What's the matter? Are you scared that I'll rape you now that I have you at my mercy?'

'Don't be ridiculous!'

'I wouldn't need to, you know,' he continued, ignoring her. 'It wouldn't take much persuasion on my part to subdue you.'

'You're very sure of yourself.'

'Somehow I don't think you'd fight me for very long.'

'You'd be surprised,' she told him defiantly.

'Will I?' he asked as he reached for her.

Even as she began to struggle Kate was aware it was a hopeless contest, one that she could never hope to win. While her brain fought a desperate battle to keep control of her body and to reject him, her senses clamoured treacherously for the touch of his lips on hers, the pressure of that lean, hard form against her. There was no way she could check the shivers of delight that ran through her as his mouth descended on hers and began a slow, sensual probing which left her weak and unresisting in his arms.

She was drowning in a sea of blissful sensations as she pressed closer to him, gasping with pleasure as his hands explored her body with languid assurance, parting her blouse from the restraining band of her skirt and moving upwards to caress her breasts. He laid siege to her senses with a practised ease that made all coherent thought leave her. She was conscious only of the flame that his touch lit within her. Her arms moved across his broad back to press him still closer to her. If this was what it meant to be a woman she gloried in the knowledge.

She felt only a tremendous sense of loss and disappointment when he finally released her and, with an effort, stepped away, pushing aside her instinctive cry of protest and her clinging arms which strove shamelessly to retain her hold on him. He surveyed her flushed face with that air of triumphant masculine overlordship that she had witnessed and so resented in the past.

'You were right—you did surprise me,' he said coolly.

'I've been wondering what it would take for that cool exterior to crack and show the real woman underneath.'

His words shocked her back to sanity like a douche of cold water down her back and she reacted instantly. 'And you couldn't resist finding out, could you?' she demanded. 'Well, I hope you're satisfied!' What had she been thinking of to let Nicholas Blake, the man she despised and distrusted more than any other, more than Jeremy even, trample down her defences so convincingly?

'It was only a kiss, for God's sake. There's no need to carry on as if no one had ever touched you before,' he said irritably.

Only a kiss, he said. Yet Jeremy's kisses had never left her as weak as this, overcome by feelings that she was barely aware existed in her, her senses still clamouring for physical fulfilment. Was it possible that he was unaware of his overwhelming effect on her? She doubted it somehow. With trembling fingers she pulled together the gaping edges of her blouse and attempted to fasten the buttons which had come undone. But her hands were shaking too badly and, as she fumbled, he said impatiently, 'Here, I'll do it,' and swiftly completed the task.

'Thank you.' She rallied, determined that if by any faint chance he *was* in ignorance of the way he aroused her, he should remain so. 'It's just that I prefer to have some say in the matter. I'm not as indiscriminate in my choice of lovers as you appear to be.'

'No, that's something I'd hesitate to accuse you of. I'm only surprised that my prim and proper secretary can talk of lovers in such an expansive fashion.' His eyes glinted wickedly as he surveyed her. 'They don't seem to have taught you very much.'

'What do you mean?' Her heart was beating uncomfortably fast.

'You lack expertise.'

'I'm sorry I don't reach your high standards,' she said sarcastically. 'But I don't suppose I've had as much practice in the art of love as you've obviously had.'

'Oh, a willingness to learn overcomes a lot of deficiencies,' he said with a casual air which infuriated her. 'And you can't deny it, Kate, you *were* willing.'

She thought of the abandon with which she had responded to his kisses only moments before and avoided his gaze. 'I won't deny it—I can't. Physically you're a very attractive man and you're experienced enough to know how to make a woman react in the right way. I grant you that.'

'But?' he prompted.

'But unlike the other women in your life I'm not so easily pleased. It takes more than a kiss to win me over.'

The devilment in his expression grew. 'Are you by any chance propositioning me? And I thought that was still the prerogative of the male. You surprise me, Kate. One minute you're fighting me off and the next——'

Her fingers itched to make contact with that mocking face, but some remnant of caution remained to stop her in time. 'You know perfectly well what I meant!'

'Oh yes, only too well. You meant that you're the sort of girl who claims to be "respectable". The sort of girl who doesn't indulge herself even with a man she admits she finds attractive.'

'There's more to love than physical attraction.'

'Were we talking about love?' he asked.

'I'd have to love a man before I slept with him. *I'm* not promiscuous,' she said sharply.

'No—I'd hardly accuse you of being free with your favours. Any man that wants you has to be prepared to make the ultimate gesture of offering you marriage. You've no intention of giving yourself to any man just for the sake of the pleasure it might bring you both. He's got to put a ring on your finger and book the church before he's allowed to touch you. And until this paragon comes along, you like to pretend you're out of bounds to any man with something else in mind.'

'You're very cynical.'

'And you're very calculating. In your way you're just as mercenary as Diana.'

'At least I'm honest about it,' she told him.

'That's a great consolation, I'm sure. But, if it makes you happy, fair enough,' he taunted her savagely. 'Tell me, Kate, have you found anyone who fits the bill yet? And *does* he make you happy? Or do you lie awake at night wondering what it would be like to have a real man take you in his arms?'

He caught her on the raw and she winced, remembering the tender restraint of Jeremy's courtship of her and how easily it had satisfied her. Then she had looked for nothing more, expected only gentle, passionless kisses, curiously lacking the excitement that she had always been led to believe accompanied true love. Now she knew only too well to what a fever pitch her senses could be excited. But passion without love was an empty thrill, a cheap sensation. Or was it? Of one thing she was sure; to get involved with Nicholas Blake was not the answer to the question. Yet how easy it would be to surrender to him, to let him envelop her in a flood of physical pleasure which would ease the pain of Jeremy's desertion and help her to forget the feeling of despair that so-called 'true' love had brought in its wake. But that course might lead to just as much disillusionment and heartbreak.

'I'm hardly likely to lose any sleep over you,' she said. 'Does that disappoint you?'

'Not at all. I can see that I'll have to try harder to convince you.'

She had no time to move away from him even if she

had wanted to. His arms came round her, moving her against the unyielding contours of his body. The hard pressure of his lips on hers aroused a passionate need of him that she could not deny. Her mouth opened and she responded mindlessly to the bruising force of his kiss, her pleasure mounting with every second. Her hands cradled his head, her fingers burying themselves in the thick, dark hair that touched his collar.

She murmured with delight as his mouth parted from hers to leave a trail of molten fire across her skin as he moved down her neck to kiss the shadowy hollows beyond it. His hands roved expertly over her, their touch bringing her alive with excitement. She was drawn into a flood-tide of sensuous enjoyment which was carrying her away into regions of pleasure that she had never dreamed could exist. In the chaste caresses she had shared with Jeremy she had never learned how to please a man, but now instinct took over and she caressed him, first tentatively, then with growing confidence, eager for him to share her pleasure.

The sudden shrill ringing of the telephone on the desk behind them brought them harshly back to reality. With an effort Nicholas dragged his head away from hers.

'Leave it. Let it ring,' she begged him.

But, with a muttered expletive, he put her from him abruptly and reached for the receiver, picking it up and identifying himself in a voice that was clear-headed and precise and gave no indication that some two seconds before he had been making violent love to his secretary. Launching immediately into a detailed analysis of a client's financial problems, he was apparently unaffected by the emotions of the last few minutes.

Kate came down to earth with considerably more of a bump, shocked into startled awareness by his sudden transition from the experienced lover, capable of launching such an assault on her senses, to the dispassionate businessman, absorbed in a new interest. A few short moments ago she had been the centre of his world, now she was disregarded. Was that how he treated all the women in his life, with so little care for their feelings? When she thought how near she had been to allowing him to break down all her defences she felt ashamed of herself. How could she have begged for his caresses? Reaction set in and, weak at the knees, she sank down into the nearest chair.

He finished his conversation and slammed down the receiver, then directed an absent look at Kate. But if she expected any reference to the interlude between them or even a return to it, she was mistaken. 'Give me the Jowett file, will you?'

So they were back with a vengeance to a boss/secretary relationship. Quite automatically Kate found herself rising to do his bidding. When he used that tone he brooked no questions or arguments. At the door she remembered and turned. 'Am I allowed out now?' she asked sweetly.

He retrieved the key from his pocket and tossed it to her. She caught it and put it in the door.

'Kate——' The command in his voice stopped her in her tracks. 'I've wasted enough time that I couldn't spare this afternoon. It won't happen again.'

'You seem very certain of that.'

'I intend to be,' he said calmly.

'Is that meant to be an apology for your behaviour?'

'No.' His gaze held hers steadily. 'I don't consider I have anything to apologise for. I just wanted to make it clear that I try, not always successfully, to keep business and pleasure apart. Do you understand me?'

'Perfectly. I must say I'm relieved to hear it. I don't

think I could cope with satisfying your jaded appetite every afternoon.'

'What makes you think you managed it today?' he enquired dangerously, but she affected not to hear the comment and left the room with undignified haste.

Back in the sanctuary of her own office she deliberately blanked off her feelings until she had completed the letters which remained to be done and then, bracing herself, took them in to him for signature. Absorbed in some paperwork, he transferred his attention to her only briefly. What had happened between them might never have been as far as he was concerned.

CHAPTER SIX

KATE returned to her office, her brain whirling at the thoughts that she had put resolutely from her until she had completed the task in hand. She supposed that the most sensible course would be to forget the whole episode as firmly as Nicholas Blake appeared to have done, to try to blot from her mind the image of herself in his arms, the feeling that for once he had seen her as an attractive and desirable woman rather than as a piece of office furniture, as indispensable, but as inanimate as the telephone which stood on his desk. No doubt she should let him assume that she was used to coping with a boss who made passes at her and that she was sophisticated enough not to take it to heart. He would only be amused if she adopted an attitude of injured pride and offered her resignation.

And yet how could she continue to work with a man whose physical presence aroused her to such an extent? It was all very well for him to flirt and go casually from one female to another as the fancy took him, entirely uninvolved and in no danger of getting his feelings even bruised, let alone as shattered as she had felt after the events of this afternoon. Was she really capable of presenting the cool, casual front that he no doubt expected of his women friends? And how was she to know whether he would decide to leave her alone in future or amuse himself further by repeating the experience any time he chose? He had assured her that it would not happen again, but could she trust him to keep his promise?

At five o'clock she was no nearer to deciding what she should do. With a resentful look at the firmly closed door leading to her employer's office she put the cover on her typewriter and left for home. Mercifully Jane was out and she was able to have the flat to herself. Her flat-mate would have been only too willing to offer good-natured advice on the problem with which Kate found herself, but she was strangely reluctant to confide a tale which would reveal her to be as susceptible to the devastating physical charms of Nicholas Blake as Jane had clearly expected her to be.

While she cooked and ate a supper that she barely tasted Kate went over the whole episode again, blushing at the memory of her willing response. How could she have fallen so readily into his arms like a ripe plum for his picking? Oh, she had made a token struggle, a mere gesture of resistance, but he had known as well as she how slight had been her attempt to get away and how ready she had been to surrender herself to his lovemaking. How could she go on working with him? She shook herself mentally. Physical attraction was a mere matter of chemistry. Nicholas Blake was an attractive man and she had responded to him the way any woman might have done. It had been a moment of unguarded weakness, one which he had exploited, but one which would not happen again, whatever blandishments he used upon her. There was no need to go to such lengths as leaving her job to avoid a repetition of the incident.

Besides, she enjoyed working for Nicholas Blake: Kate freely admitted it. After the initial, cautious days when he had tested her intelligence and ability to cope in a number of taxing situations, Nicholas had given her more and more responsibility and she had appreciated his growing trust and confidence in her. Where would she find a job that suited her as well as this one? Indeed, after all the trouble that she had experienced in getting a job at all, this one ought to be doubly precious.

Yet, after marshalling every argument and excuse she could think of in support of staying with Nicholas, Kate knew that for her own peace of mind she must leave him. It was all very well telling herself that the application of mind over matter could resist the physical magnetism he held for her, but she knew that he had only to take her in his arms again and she would weaken. There was more to life than being just another of Nicholas' mistresses, she told herself firmly. She would hand in her notice the next day. The decision made, she took herself off to bed, where, despite her resolution not to dwell on the matter, she spent a sleepless night worrying about how he would react to the news.

As it happened she need not have worried. Arriving early at the office she had got as far as typing her brief letter of resignation and was putting it in an envelope when she realised that Nicholas had told her the previous morning that he was visiting a client in Sussex and that he would be away all day. In all that had followed since she had forgotten. She shrugged. That meant that she would not have the satisfaction of handing him the missive personally, but she was secretly relieved not to have to face him. His temper was uncertain at the best of times and she hardly thought that he would take the news calmly. When she left to go that afternoon she placed the envelope with his name upon it firmly in the centre of his desk where he could not fail to see it.

Yet, next day, it seemed that it must after all have escaped his attention. He was already hard at work in his office when Kate arrived and, apart from a brief word of thanks when she carried in his morning cup of coffee, he ignored her. If he had read the letter he made no mention of it, even when he called her in for dictation. Was it possible that it had somehow gone astray? Kate puzzled. She looked at the mass of papers in front of him, but failed to discover her own letter among them. As he dismissed her she plucked up the courage to ask him about it.

'Ah, yes, your letter.' He reached to one side, picked up a single sheet of paper and studied it as if he had not seen it before. There was a tight, disapproving look to his mouth and Kate quailed inwardly. 'You didn't have the courage to deliver it in person, did you? Just left it like a thief in the night.'

'You weren't in yesterday.'

'And you couldn't wait a day before handing in your resignation.' The grey eyes were studying her now and she flinched under his scrutiny. 'Why do you want to go?'

'I should have thought that was obvious.'

He did not pretend to misunderstand her. 'All because of a couple of casual kisses? They meant nothing to me—to either of us. Don't you think you're being a little melodramatic?'

She might have known that it would mean nothing to him. What had been a totally shattering mental and physical experience to her had been just another casual encounter to him. His attitude sickened her. It was as well that she was leaving him.

'No, I don't think I'm being melodramatic,' she said.

He shrugged. 'You should feel complimented. I'm not usually so easily distracted in the office.'

'That's typical of your attitude,' Kate accused him. 'You're so—so careless about everything.'

'If I was as careless as you believe I'd hardly have got where I am today.' He paused, then asked, 'How do you think I got to be head of this firm?'

She had never considered the question. He filled the position with the confident assurance of a far older man.

It was as if he held the office by divine right. She could not ever imagine Nicholas Blake struggling for anything. He was ambitious, yes, but he was a man who achieved his ambitions apparently without effort. Her face mirrored her puzzlement as she frowned and finally admitted, 'I don't know. I've never thought about it.'

'Well, think about it now,' he told her impatiently.

She realised how little she knew of him and his background. She could not envisage him in any environment except the one he dominated so successfully. Not for him the steady toil upwards, the yearly minuscule increases in salary until middle age brought a reasonable degree of success and power and a worthy reputation in his field. He had got too far too soon. She dimly remembered Jane telling her that he had made his empire in ten years, but how he achieved it she was totally ignorant.

'I don't know,' she said again.

He thrust back his chair and walked over to the window. He was silent for a moment as he stood gazing out over the tightly packed mass of buildings with the dome of St Paul's rising in its midst that represented the commercial heart of London. Then he turned to her again. 'Would it surprise you to learn that fifteen years ago I had nothing? No money in the bank, no fancy education, no public school background giving me endless contacts in big business to draw upon. I had just my wits and a driving need to prove myself by getting on in the world. It proved the best combination imaginable. You're looking surprised, Kate. Do you suspect shady dealing?'

'No,' she said firmly. She knew enough of Nicholas Blake's business affairs by now to realise that he would never cheat or bend the truth for his own advantage. He offered his clients frankness and plain speaking, whether they appreciated it or not. In a commercial world where a man's world was his bond and a deal representing thousands of pounds could still be concluded on nothing more concrete than a handshake he was known for his scrupulous, even brutal honesty. 'How *did* you manage it?' she asked.

'By damned hard work.' His face shadowed at the memory of those days. 'I thought of nobody and nothing except my work. I used to put in a hard day at a City stockbrokers, then go home to my digs and study until the early hours of the morning. I ate and drank finance.' He laughed. 'I even started to dream about the Stock Market! But it all paid off in the end. I moved up the ladder two rungs at a time and five years later I was able to set up on my own. Since then I've enjoyed a fair degree of affluence and the pleasures it brings with it.'

Enjoyed was the right word, thought Kate, when she considered that the fruits of success included Diana Kendall and other beautiful women. He would not reject such temptations when they were offered to him. Why should he?

'So,' she said calmly, 'you've made it. Congratulations. So what?'

'My life in the past fifteen years would make a useful lesson in how not to waste time—in the office at least.' A flicker of devilry sparked in the grey glance. 'I'm merely assuring you that your jealously guarded virtue is safe. I don't intend to spend my time in hot pursuit of your admittedly desirable body around the office. Does that set your mind at rest?'

'How can I be sure of that?'

His glance narrowed and roved over her with a keen penetration that discomfited her. 'Aren't you slightly overestimating your attributes, Kate?' he enquired dangerously. 'Attractive you may be, but I don't recall saying that you were unique in that respect.'

Kate was silent. She was no match for him when it

came to offering calculated insults.

He glanced at the letter of resignation in his hand. 'If, at any time in the future, you come up with what I consider to be a valid reason for leaving my employment, I'll give it my close attention. Meanwhile you'll continue to work for me.' He tore the sheet of paper in half and tossed the pieces towards her. The movement reminded her vividly of the time when she had attempted something similar and thrown the pieces of his business card in his face. The knowledge hung between them as he intended it should. 'You're not the only one to make extravagant gestures,' he taunted her softly.

And there the matter rested. Strangely, although he had wrought havoc with her nervous system once again and had worsted her in yet another confrontation, Kate was almost relieved that the interview had gone that way. The knowledge that she was staying in her job left her practically lightheaded with relief, although she found it impossible to analyse why and gave up trying in the end. She settled back again into the routine of office life as if there had never been anything untoward between herself and Nicholas Blake. And indeed, occasionally, looking at the brisk yet cool façade that he presented to her in the days and weeks following her abortive attempt to resign, she wondered if this could be the same man who had kissed her into a state of almost total surrender. Contrarily she felt piqued by the ease with which he managed to treat her with total indifference. She could certainly never fail to be aware of the spell he held over her senses.

Diana Kendall still featured heavily in his social life despite what he had said to Kate about her. It seemed that she amused him. With a cynicism that surprised herself she assumed that this was what life was really all about: the need to use people without necessarily allowing yourself to be used in turn. It was a game which Nicholas Blake was a past expert at. Diana served his purposes admirably and would continue to do so until he found her demands for attention begin to cloy and ditched her with the minimum of heart-searching. Or perhaps this time, for all his fine words to the contrary, he intended to take up the matrimonial bait being offered to him and Diana would lead him to the altar? Kate found the thought strangely depressing and, as often as it surfaced, she pushed it firmly to the back of her mind. Why should she worry about Nicholas Blake's love life? After all, he never gave a thought to hers.

But in making that assumption it seemed that she had miscalculated again. One day, while Nicholas was absent on one of his lightning trips across the Atlantic, she was working late at the office trying desperately to sort out queries which would require his immediate attention on his return. She was sitting at Nicholas' desk wrinkling her nose at a highly-scented lilac envelope, addressed in Diana's sprawling writing and marked 'personal', and wondering whether it merited inclusion in the urgent pile when an amused voice from the doorway cut in on her thoughts.

'After five o'clock and still hard at it, I see. What a treasure of a secretary I have!'

She started and dropped Diana's letter as if it had suddenly become red-hot.

'I hope I pay you overtime for all this dedication to my interests.' He was leaning against the doorpost surveying her flushed face and only too well aware who had written the letter which she had been holding.

She got to her feet, struggling for composure, and only made matters worse by telling him, 'I wasn't expecting you back until tomorrow.'

'Obviously not.' The amusement in his tone deepened.

'I tied things up quicker than I anticipated and caught an earlier flight. I expected you to have left the office by the time I arrived, so there didn't seem any point in letting you know the change of plan.'

He was looking his usual cool, immaculate self, the formality of the dark suit he wore enhancing his lean attraction, the crisp whiteness of his shirt contrasting against the tan of his face. He looked as if he had just spent a week soaking up the sun and relaxing in the Bahamas or some other sun-spot favoured by the jet-set. Instead, Kate knew that he had completed a taxing schedule of appointments which she herself had fixed for him. He ought to be exhausted, yet, as always, he thrived on the experience. It was almost unfair, she thought.

She explained hastily, 'I was trying to make sure that you saw the most important letters first when you got back.'

'Thoughtful of you,' he observed, entering the room and tossing his briefcase on to a chair. 'But the rest can wait until tomorrow now. Get your coat—I'm taking you out to dinner.'

'I beg your pardon?'

'You heard what I said.'

'But I don't want to have dinner with you,' Kate lied vehemently.

'I don't remember asking you whether you wanted to or not.' The grey eyes glinted with that devilry that she had long ago decided was a compelling part of his charm and a feature of his personality that she was no more capable than any other woman of resisting, try as she might. 'In my usual overbearing way I'm running true to form and ordering you to have dinner with me tonight.'

She glanced down at the neat blouse and skirt she was wearing. They were eminently suitable for the office, but hardly good enough for dining out with someone like

Nicholas who frequented the best restaurants in town. 'But I'm not dressed for eating out,' she protested.

His glance surveyed her briefly. 'You look fine to me,' he told her. 'Stop making excuses.'

'But——' she began to protest half-heartedly again.

'What's the matter? Are you still scared of me?'

'No, but——'

'Are you thinking what your boy-friend will say?'

'No.'

'Then there's no problem, is there?' he said coolly. He looked at his watch. 'I haven't eaten anything apart from an airline's plastic apology for a meal since early this morning and I'm hungry. I expect you are too. You've got three minutes. I'll book a table while you go and get your coat. O.K.?'

Their glances caught and held. Kate's last remnants of resistance fell away. 'O.K.,' she said meekly, capitulating as they had both known she always would. After all, what was she arguing about? A shared meal between boss and secretary meant nothing beyond the chance for her to acquaint Nicholas with what had been happening in the office while he had been away.

Looking at her flushed, eager face in the mirror of the cloakroom as she hastily tidied her hair and did a quick repair job on her make-up, she wondered who she was trying to fool. She was as eager as a girl on her very first date, breathless with anticipation of the evening ahead. 'Pull yourself together, girl,' she told herself sternly. 'This isn't going to lead anywhere and, what's more, you don't want it to. Remember what happened last time you let your feelings run away with you.' Yet she returned to Nicholas' office with a light step and a feeling of happiness that increased when she saw that, although he had glanced at some of the letters on his desk in her absence, Diana Kendall's letter remained unopened.

'Ready? Good.' He got to his feet and escorted her to the door. As they came out of the lift together and crossed the reception area the night security guard bade them a rather surprised 'Goodnight'. It would be all over the building tomorrow that she and the great man had been seen leaving together, Kate thought ruefully, as she followed Nicholas to where his gleaming black Porsche hugged the kerb.

He drove well, handling the powerful car with a control and sureness of touch that she could not help but admire. She might have known that he would notice.

'Taking back all those rude remarks you once made about my driving?' he asked.

'Amending them slightly,' she said, and he laughed at the admission.

It was not long before they drew up outside a small, discreetly-lit restaurant in one of the side streets not far from the West End.

'I thought you'd go for good food as well as atmosphere and this place has both,' Nicholas informed her as he led her inside.

And what exactly did he mean by that? she wondered, as they were greeted by a smiling, bowing head-waiter, who, as she might have known, found it nothing but an honour to provide Nicholas Blake with a table at such short notice. Once comfortably seated and provided with a menu which offered every out of season delicacy she could have wished for, Kate spared a thought for her flat-mate, in all probability sitting down to beans on toast for the third time that week. What would Jane say when she heard about this little episode? Probably put two and two together and make six. Kate frowned.

Nicholas, ever observant, noticed and, after they had ordered, queried with a wicked smile, 'Well, will he be annoyed when you tell him? Or won't you tell him?'

'Tell who?' she asked stupidly, not understanding him.

'The attentive boy-friend I'm sure you must possess. Will he be waiting to wring my neck tomorrow morning or will you preserve a discreet silence and not mention it?'

She dodged the issue. 'What is there to tell? My boss takes me out for a meal so that I can bring him up to date on what's been happening in the office while he's been away. Is that a cause for scandal?'

He shrugged. 'Anyone I escort seems the target for talk,' he said cynically. 'The gossip columnists take an unhealthy interest in my activities.'

And so did she, thought Kate guiltily, as she remembered the number of times recently she had avidly devoured the details of his latest jaunt with Diana. Why she had done so she hardly knew herself and she had certainly no intention of revealing to *him*. 'Oh, I hardly think your secretary counts as food for the newspapers.'

'You'd be surprised. I'm not given to wining and dining my staff.'

A shadow of misgiving hit her at his words, but she responded casually enough. 'So why start now? You could have waited until tomorrow to hear the office news. In fact, if I'd left at five o'clock on the dot as I'm supposed to do, you'd have to have waited.'

His smile glinted briefly, mischievously. 'But you didn't leave early. And here we are. Life is full of unexpected surprises.' He paused as a waiter served their steaks and another brought the wine he had chosen for them, then continued, 'Besides, who said I wanted to hear the office news from you? I can think of better things to discuss with an attractive girl, even if she is my secretary.'

She was faintly proud of the cool way she managed to ask, 'Are you trying to flirt with me?' although the words themselves might be naïve.

'Still suspecting my motives, Kate?'

'Aren't I right to do so? The world must be full of girls who fell for a charming load of nonsense and regretted it afterwards.'

'And you've no intention of adding to the number?' he asked quizzically, studying her with a sudden intentness which lent a curious weight to his words.

'Certainly not!'

He smiled full at her and involuntarily she responded, incapable of resisting the way his normally harsh features relaxed and became entirely human. Gone was the remote, austere man for whom she had worked for the last few weeks and in his place was the Nicholas who knew only too well how to pursue and flatter his quarry, the Nicholas who had demonstrated to Kate with such expertise that he could break down any defences a woman cared to muster against him.

'That was why you put up a token fight before agreeing to have dinner with me?'

'If you like.'

'Yet you came.'

'It's a free meal at a good restaurant and I'm as fond of my food as the next girl,' she said.

'You won't convince me that you're just a freebooter. I think I know you a little too well for that.'

She raised a sceptical eyebrow at him. Perhaps it was the wine that was going to her head, but she felt suddenly reckless. She was enjoying this verbal fencing as much as he was and she was reluctant to bring it to an end. 'And how well do you know me?' she asked casually. 'Perhaps you'd like to give me a quick run-down on my character?' She turned from him to study the sweets trolley and select a portion of a creamy confection crowned with fresh strawberries.

He waited until she was served and then helped himself to cheese, taking his time and deliberately keeping her waiting for his answer. 'I'll tell you some time. But not tonight.'

'Not confident in your own judgment?' she ventured teasingly.

'I find it pays never to be too sure of myself when dealing with a woman,' he said. 'They're too capricious for that. One has always to be prepared to change with the prevailing wind.'

'That's a rather sweeping statement, isn't it?'

He mocked her. 'Come now, Kate. You're surely not suggesting that your sex is boringly predictable?'

'No, merely that we're as capable as you are of making reasoned judgments.'

'You mean you have lightning instinctive reactions and then invent logical reasons to support them.'

'Perhaps,' she conceded, not prepared to take the argument further than the gentle banter which they had used so far.

He laughed with genuine amusement. 'Fighting shy?' he asked.

She responded with a mock demure smile. 'I refuse to be drawn on the subject. I'm not going to fight you tonight.' She speared a portion of the creamy gateau on her plate and added impishly, 'Besides, I was always taught that it's wrong to bite the hand that feeds you.'

'Cupboard love? I must take you out more often. Who knows the rewards that might be in store for me?'

His eyes roved over her, the meaning behind his words unmistakable. Yet she was triumphant rather than offended. She might have none of the surface glamour of Diana Kendall, but she could arouse his masculine interest without such aids. For this brief space of time she was superior to Diana or any other girl in Nicholas' past, because, right now, *she* had his sole interest and attention. And the knowledge filled her with a glow of well-being that seemed entirely right.

'Come and dance,' he commanded and, lost in a haze of good food, wine and happiness, she needed no urging to get to her feet and make her way with him to the tiny, dimly-lit dais where several couples were already moving to the sound of the music. He was a good dancer, responding instinctively to the rhythm and holding her lightly but firmly in his arms as they circled the floor. His touch stirred her senses to an awareness against which she had been struggling all evening that Nicholas Blake was the most excitingly virile man that she had ever met. In the distant background, almost as if it was another planet, she was dimly aware of all the sights and sounds of the restaurant and the other dancers, but she was alive only to the heady bliss of being in his arms.

The tempo changed, the music becoming slower and dreamier, and she did not resist when he pulled her close to him, abandoning the last remnants of caution as she surrendered to the seductive spell of the music and gave in to the overwhelming temptation to twine her arms round his neck. If she had a conscious thought it was the wish that this could go on for ever. She caught the lemony tang of his aftershave as he bent his head closer and a tremor of delight shook her as his lips brushed hers, first gently, then with a passion that excited and stirred a greater response in her. He pressed her still closer to him, moulding her against the hard contours of his body and making her thrillingly aware that she had awakened a need in him as great as he had aroused in her.

Then there was a sudden blinding flash of light that shocked them both back to reality. Abruptly released from the comforting hold of Nicholas' arms, Kate turned, bewildered, to see a man, camera in hand, run towards the door which led to the street and disappear through it. Nicholas started in pursuit, but returned a few seconds later looking furious, having given up the chase.

'These blasted photographers!' he complained. 'I wonder how he knew I was here. Someone must have tipped him off.' He glanced angrily around. 'And if I find out who it was there'll be hell to pay!'

Kate was still reeling from the shock. 'You mean he was from a newspaper?' she asked, confused.

'A freelance. I've had rows with him before now. If I'd caught him that film wouldn't have reached Fleet Street and he knew it—that's why he disappeared so quickly. He'll know where to sell the picture. We'll be featured across half the gossip pages tomorrow morning.'

The reality of the situation brought a cold burst of sanity to her. What had she done? Tonight she had let down her defences and relaxed in Nicholas Blake's arms. Tomorrow she would be splashed across the pages of the popular press as the latest girl in the life, and therefore by insinuation the bed, of 'the City's most eligible bachelor'. She felt suddenly sick. Had Nicholas really not known that the photographer was there? Oh, he had run after him and seemed angry at the intrusion, but perhaps it had all been an act. Diana was becoming too pressing in her attentions and he had decided to show her that she had to toe the line or be replaced. What a fool she had been to suppose that Nicholas would treat his secretary's feelings any differently from anyone else in his life.

The spell was shattered now, the moments of easy intimacy between them had gone. She hated Nicholas Blake, but she hated herself more. How could she have fallen for such a trick? She wished with all her heart that she had never come.

She gathered the shreds of her dignity around her. 'Please, take me home,' she asked him.

He started to remonstrate, then after a look at her set face agreed. He summoned the waiter and signed the bill, then led Kate out of the restaurant.

The thought of the shared drive home was almost too much to bear. 'Perhaps you'd be good enough to get me a taxi?' she asked coldly as he felt in his pocket for the car keys.

'Don't be a fool. I'll drive you home.'

'I'd rather you didn't,' she said tautly. 'I think I've been through enough in your company tonight.'

In the half-light of the street lamps she could not see his expression, but she sensed that he was checking his temper with difficulty. Yet his voice was cool enough, with an iciness to it which brought back memories of other encounters at which Kate had come off worst. 'I've no intention of staging a stand-up row with you on a street corner. Get in the car and we'll discuss whatever's biting you in a more civilised fashion.'

'No, it would never do for the gossip columnists to find you with a woman who'd taken exception to your famous technique for getting your own way, would it?'

She flung the words at him, determined to provoke a reaction, and got one that she hardly expected. He wasted no time arguing but grabbed her forcibly and, opening the car door, bundled her inside. He had crossed in front of the car and was in the driver's seat before she had fathomed which catch released the door, and now it was too late to escape. She knew that she was no match for his superior strength—he had already proved that successfully.

'Where to?'

It would have been childish to refuse to answer him, so she gave him her address. He drove off, the burst of speed and crash of gears indicating more clearly than anything he could have said what kind of mood he was in. On the outskirts of town he turned into a tree-lined road and brought the car to a sudden halt. Switching off the ignition, he turned to her. 'Right. You've had a chance to cool down a little. Perhaps you'd like to explain the little act you put on back there.'

'There's nothing to explain. I think you're despicable, Nicholas Blake!'

'Evidently,' he said, unmoved. 'But you managed to hide your feelings successfully earlier this evening. Why the sudden change of mood?'

'That was before I realised you had an ulterior motive in asking me to have dinner with you.'

He was being eminently reasonable, as if talking to a muddled six-year-old. 'As a matter of fact I had, but I fail to see how you realised.'

'I'm not *that* stupid. I suppose you assumed I'd think the photographer was there by accident?'

'Photographer? Kate, what the hell are you talking about?'

'The photographer you planted there to take a picture of us together. "Dashing Nicholas Blake with his latest conquest." Do you really think Diana would be so easily discouraged? Or was the idea just to make her jealous?'

'You think I set it up?' he demanded.

'Didn't you?' she said, aware of the fury in his voice, but careless of the consequences.

'No, I didn't, although I don't know why I'm bothering to deny it. My God, you must have a low opinion of me to think that I'd stoop to that sort of trick!'

'And you must think me very naïve, if you gambled on fooling me like that,' she retorted. 'I wondered why you were so keen to take me out to dinner. When that photographer appeared it dawned on me.'

'It didn't occur to you that I might have something else in mind?' he enquired.

'Should it have done?'

'Your opinion of my morals seems to be rock bottom. Surely I wouldn't stop at seducing my secretary along the way.' The cold contempt in his tone stung her. 'Or would I have lured you to my flat for that?'

He made the question sound like an accusation and she felt the first tiny seeds of doubt in her mind. Could she have been wrong? 'I'm sorry——' She forced the words out. 'I may have misjudged you. It was just that——'

'I may have misjudged you,' he mimicked her harshly. 'An apology, Kate? That's big of you. I can leave the court without a stain on my character, can I? Or are you just making a qualified retraction?'

She was silent.

'To hell with your apology. If I'm cast as the villain of the piece I may as well justify my reputation.' He reached for her in the darkness and, before she could guess his intention and attempt to break free, his mouth had descended on hers, brutal in its punishment. It was more than she was capable of to try to fight him and, unresisting, she suffered the bruising mastery of his lips on hers and rested limply in his arms.

He raised his head, his eyes raking her face. 'Damn you, Kate, why do you always make me lose my temper with you?' he asked and, without waiting for an answer, his mouth came down again on hers with something akin to desperation. This time his kiss was gentle, his touch almost butterfly soft as his lips left hers and traced a line of awareness along her cheekbone to nibble her earlobe, lingering with tantalising slowness before descending to the smooth column of her neck and the dark hollows beyond.

Mindlessly Kate let the waves of sensation drift over her, building up until her whole body felt alive at his touch. His arms were around her, holding her close to him, closer than they had been on the dance floor half an hour before. But then the presence of the other dancers had served as a check on her inclination to demand more of him, to offer him all that was hers to offer. Now the only barrier between them was a rapidly fading inner voice which told her that she would regret it if she gave in to him.

She felt as if he had hit her when he suddenly released her and asked her furiously, 'Does that reinforce your opinion of me?'

Without waiting for an answer he turned the key in the ignition with an angry jerk of the hand and set the car in motion. 'You'd better tidy yourself up,' he told her brusquely. 'You look as if you've been dragged through a hedge backwards!'

And felt as if she had, thanks to him, she thought, as, with unsteady hands, she straightened her clothes and tried to recover enough to issue brief directions to him as to how to reach her flat. She was too shaken to attempt any form of verbal retaliation and, to judge from his tight-lipped expression, it would hardly be well received.

The sleek black car drew up outside her flat with a squeal of brakes. He reached across her to open the door for her and said, as if it was an effort for him to sound civil, 'I'll see you in the morning and, if you know what's good for you, don't put me to the trouble of coming to get you if you don't turn up.' The words held a threat of further punishment.

She got out of the car and slammed the door behind her in wordless protest. Even before she had reached the door of the flat she heard the powerful roar of the engine as he drove off into the distance. Shakily she put the key in the lock and turned it on the second attempt, blinking back the hot tears that welled up in her eyes.

The light was still on in the sitting room and Jane was curled up on the sofa reading a thriller.

'So what happened to you, then? You can't have been working until this time. Did a handsome millionaire sweep you——' She broke off as she saw the tears on Kate's cheeks. 'What happened, love? Look, sit down and hang on a tick.' She pushed her friend, unresisting, into an armchair by the fire and disappeared into the kitchen, returning a moment later with a glass which she thrust at Kate. 'Drink this brandy.'

'No, it's all right,' Kate sniffed, trying to stem the flood. 'I'll be all right in a bit.'

'Drink it,' her friend insisted. 'You've obviously had a shock of some kind.'

She drained the glass obediently and coughed as the liquid burned a fiery path down her throat. Yet it took the icy chill from her which had gripped her since she had staggered from Nicholas' car and she was grateful for that at least.

'Do you feel like telling me about it?' Jane asked. 'Will it help?'

Kate summoned up a watery smile. 'Nothing and nobody could help, but I'll tell you anyway.' And she gave her friend a swift account of the events of the evening.

Jane listened without interrupting, her eyes wide. When Kate had finished she gave a low whistle of astonishment. 'My, you have got yourself into a mess! You don't think he's really capable of using you just to get back at Diana, do you?'

'When I'm thinking rationally, no,' Kate admitted. 'He hates gossip columnists and does everything he can to avoid them normally. But tonight I wasn't thinking rationally.'

'Obviously not,' her friend said drily. 'He must pack quite a punch when he's trying to charm a woman.'

'Well, he didn't charm me,' Kate insisted. 'I hate Nicholas Blake. He's the most scheming, despicable man I've ever met!'

'Methinks the lady doth protest too much,' said Jane, as she had on a previous occasion. 'But have you thought why he did take you out tonight if it wasn't just to make Diana jealous?'

'God knows.' Kate gave a weary sigh. 'He said he had an ulterior motive, but what it could be is beyond me. I suppose he'll sack me tomorrow.'

'Why are you so worried about it, if you dislike him so much?' Jane asked teasingly.

'I'm not. I'll be as glad to see the back of him as he will be to get rid of me.' With those defiant words Kate took herself off to bed. Where, as she drifted off into a sleep of utter exhaustion, her last thoughts were of Nicholas Blake. She had told Jane she would be glad never to see him again, but she was all too aware that was the last thing in the world that she wanted.

CHAPTER SEVEN

'WELL, you certainly excelled yourself last night.' Jane entered Kate's room the next morning bearing a cup of tea in one hand and the morning paper in the other. 'Better drink your tea first. You'll need something to steady your nerves.'

Kate ignored the advice and made a grab for the paper. 'Is there a photograph? What's it like? Is it as bad as I thought?'

'That,' said Jane, opening the paper at the appropriate page and looking carefully at it, 'is a matter of opinion. It's quite a good likeness of you. Nicholas Blake looks his usual dashing self. And to judge from the look on your face you can't hate the man quite as much as you claim to do.'

'Let me see.' Impatiently Kate tore the paper from her friend and studied it anxiously. Horrors, it was ten times worse than she could ever have imagined! Was the dreamy-eyed, besotted-looking female gazing up into Nicholas Blake's handsome face and clinging possessively to him really her? 'Oh, Jane, how awful!'

'Have you seen what it says underneath?'

She read the caption hastily. It was headed 'Mystery date for Nicholas Blake' and went on to drop coy hints that Diana Kendall had been supplanted as Number One in the harem. Kate tossed it aside. 'What a mess! Jane, what am I going to do? How can I face him this morning after that?'

'With difficulty, I imagine.' Jane was sympathetic but unhelpful. 'It'll all blow over in a few days, I expect. He must be used to this sort of thing.'

'Not having his name coupled with his staff, he isn't. He warned me not to get ideas along those lines when he took me on.'

'Then he shouldn't take you out to expensive restaurants for dinner, should he?' Jane pointed out practically. 'Anyway, if you don't hurry up and get ready for work, you'll have him pounding on the door to drag you there by the short hairs.'

Kate supposed her flat-mate was talking sense, but as she dragged herself reluctantly across reception and towards the lift to her office she felt less inclined to agree, particularly when she was almost certain that the downstairs receptionist responded to her 'Good morning' with a good deal more interest than usual. On her own floor two secretaries stopped their animated conversation when they saw her and looked uncomfortable, and Kate did not need to be super-intelligent to guess what—or rather who—had been the person they had been talking about. Damn Nicholas Blake for putting her in such an unenviable position!

It was too much to expect that he might attempt to apologise for his behaviour and, at first, Kate wondered if he was intending to mention last night's little episode at all as he bade her a reserved 'Good morning' and proceeded to get down to work as usual. So much for the nerve it had taken to present herself in his office with notebook and pencil in hand, prepared to take dictation as if the events of last night were commonplace to her. In an effort to dispel the abandoned image she had presented then she had dressed carefully in a neat but sombre black dress that she had to acknowledge was not one of her best buys. Jane, well-meaning but tactless, had told her that it made her look like an old-fashioned waitress 'minus white pinafore'.

Nicholas Blake was even less complimentary. As she turned to leave his office after a hard hour's dictation he glanced up, apparently taking her in for the first time. 'In mourning for your lost reputation, Kate?' he queried, looking faintly amused.

'I might have known that you'd treat it like a joke,' she said bitterly.

'What other way is there of looking at it? It was unfortunate, but it can't be helped.'

'Unfortunate for me, perhaps. It just added to your reputation, didn't it?'

He shrugged. 'That kind of reputation doesn't particularly interest me. And being bitter about it won't help you to put it out of your mind either.'

'I can't forget it as easily as that,' she flung at him. 'I don't exactly enjoy facing the fact that everyone in the office thinks that I'm the latest girl to keep your sheets warm for you. *You* don't have to put up with the snide remarks and knowing looks.'

'I think you might have suffered them anyway,' he told her.

'I don't understand.'

He gestured impatiently towards a chair. 'For God's sake, sit down instead of hovering like a schoolgirl up before the headmaster!' When she had complied and perched uncomfortably on the edge of a straight-backed chair by his desk, he continued, 'You may remember at one point in our—conversation—last night that you accused me of having an ulterior motive for taking you out. As a matter of fact I had, but, as I tried somewhat less than successfully to explain to you, it wasn't the reason you seized upon.' He got up and prowled to the window where he remained silently studying the view for long enough for Kate's interest to be caught and provoked by what he said. She supposed that was his intention; he liked to play cat and mouse with her. She wondered what was coming next.

'I'll admit I had my doubts when I gave you the job,' he went on, suddenly turning to her again. 'But I'm seldom wrong when I back a hunch. You've shaped up very well and I've been able to leave a lot of things to you that before I'd have done myself. You're the first secretary I've had who's been able to work on her own initiative and yet not put a foot wrong.'

'I—I——' Kate could have kicked herself. Where was her self-control? Instead of coolly accepting the praise as her due here she was blushing and stammering like the schoolgirl he had called her. 'Thank you,' she managed at last. Where was all this leading?

'I don't waste time with idle compliments,' he assured her. 'I've always thought that actions speak louder than words.' He noticed the colour in her cheeks and added with a hint of wickedness, 'In more senses than one.'

She ignored the dig. 'So?' she asked with a fair assumption of a calm she was far from feeling.

'So I decided to promote you, give you a substantial rise in salary and make you my personal assistant. The typing and filing and most of the day-to-day routine can be handled by someone else and you can concentrate in future on helping with the important stuff which, I suspect, you enjoy more anyway.'

So she had a future with him, did she? Kate was not sure whether to be consoled or horrified by the prospect of even closer contact with him.

He went on, 'I'd worked it out while I was over in the States and was going to break it to you today. When I got back late last night and found you still working it occurred to me that dinner with you might be as good an opportunity as any to tell you about the state of things.'

'I see.' She was stunned. Even amid the whirl that her

thoughts were in she noticed that he intended telling her rather than asking her about the new job. The arrangement suited him, therefore it had to suit her, whether she approved of it or not. But that was unfair. How could she feel anything but delighted at the prospect of a pay rise and a more interesting job? If a doubt niggled at her at the wisdom of seeking a closer involvement with Nicholas Blake she pushed it firmly aside. 'It's very kind of you,' she said carefully. 'Thank you.'

He laughed, his handsome face alight with amusement. 'No, not kind. I'm afraid pure self-interest motivated the decision,' he told her.

'And was it self-interest that caused you to take such a long time breaking the news to me last night?' she asked him carefully. 'I don't recall you raising the subject over dinner.'

The grey gaze held hers with a sudden devilry that she found disturbing. 'Possibly. I was going to tell you over coffee, but I was momentarily—diverted. Dancing with a beautiful woman doesn't always present the right opportunity for a business discussion. And afterwards, if you remember, you were too busy accusing me of every villainy under the sun to listen to anything I had to say in my defence or otherwise.'

'Oh,' she said flatly. It sounded all too plausible not to be true. Nicholas Blake was not likely to concoct a story and a job offer like that just to preserve his good name in his secretary's eyes.

'The offer still stands despite the less than flattering opinion of me you expressed last night. Well?'

At that moment the telephone on his desk began to ring. He ignored it, his attention focussed on Kate. In the pent-up silence between them the ringing sounded unnaturally loud. She picked up the receiver and answered it. 'It's Diana,' she said, her voice carefully expressionless as she held out the receiver to him. 'She says she couldn't get you at home.'

'Tell her I'm out,' he snapped, careless as to whether his voice could be heard at the other end of the line. 'I don't want to be bothered with her.'

She conveyed the message as diplomatically as possible, but it did not satisfy Diana, who had obviously caught the end of his remark. 'I'm sorry, Mr Blake really isn't——' Kate was arguing when firm fingers took the receiver impatiently from her.

'Diana, I'm busy and I've no time for you now.' Not discouraged, the shrill voice at the other end went on. Kate saw his face darken with anger and guessed that he was being taken to task for his part in last night's proceedings, possibly an unwise move unless Diana was extremely sure of herself. Nicholas listened, his expression growing grimmer by the second, then in a voice chillier than he had ever addressed to Kate, he said, 'Who I take to my bed is a matter for me and the lady concerned. I'll thank you to remember that in future.' The receiver slammed down on the rest and, still frowning, he turned to Kate as if the interruption had never taken place. 'Well?' he demanded.

She smiled at him, strangely elated by the short, sharp way he had dispensed with Diana, even at the expense of her own reputation. 'I accept. I'd be a fool not to.'

'A lot of people will think you're a fool to take me on. I'm not an easy man to work for, I'll admit that.'

'I'm not worried,' she told him.

'There'll be plenty who'll say you owe the promotion to, how shall I put it, services rendered elsewhere than the office.'

She shrugged. 'If I'm to be saddled with the reputation of being your mistress, I may as well enjoy the profits that ensue.'

He moved closer to her and she was aware of her senses stirring dangerously as she caught the remembered scent of his cologne. 'Some women might think that sharing my bed *was* one of the pluses about that situation.'

'I'm not some women,' she said firmly, standing her ground, although to give way to the temptation to put the length of the room between herself and him might have been the more sensible course.

'No. I became aware of that last night.'

'Were you disappointed?'

'I wouldn't say that.' He put one hand under her chin, forcing her to look up at him. Taking his time as he studied her face as if he had never seen it before, taking in the tip-tilted nose, the high cheekbones, the dark, slightly apprehensive eyes and dwelling on the soft, all too vulnerable set of her mouth. She quivered slightly as she stood, unresisting, under his touch, her heart thudding so loudly she was afraid that he would hear it. 'You surprised me last night. You pack quite a punch, don't you?'

'I'm glad you think so,' she said flippantly. His mouth was only inches away from hers. Was he going to kiss her? If he did there was no way she could avoid responding. Talking like this with Nicholas Blake was like playing with dynamite, but it was giving her an exhilaration that no man had ever made her feel before.

'We'll have to explore the depths of your character further some time.' His voice promised a lot, but he was not going to kiss her. He let her go, not without reluctance, she thought. 'But, for the present, we've got work to do.'

He stepped away from her and sat down behind the desk. She felt ridiculously disappointed, like a child deprived of its favourite chocolate bar. Damn him, did he tantalise her on purpose, or was he unaware of the feelings he aroused in her? She did not think so, somehow. There was nothing Nicholas Blake did not know about how to handle a woman.

'Organise someone from the typing pool to come in and do the basics,' he instructed her. 'It'll be a while before you can ditch it completely, but, in the meantime, I'll be breaking you in gradually on the tougher stuff. Your first assignment, though, will be a more traditionally feminine one.'

'Indeed?' she asked warily.

He smiled. 'Don't get ideas, Kate. I want you to act as my hostess at a small dinner-party I'm giving for one of my business associates. He's not a bad old stick, but he's used to getting his own way. He can be led, but not driven, and he resents being told outright what to do. Do you think you could cope with him?'

'It's a type I've had a little experience with lately,' Kate said demurely.

'And with reasonable success.' His hand acknowledged the hit. 'You won't have to do any cooking or anything—that will be handled by a firm of caterers I always use. They're totally reliable and there won't be any problems about that. All you have to do is look elegant and respond intelligently to anything Sir Geoffrey says as well as keeping everyone else happy.'

'Sir Geoffrey?'

'Sir Geoffrey Markham, the industrialist. His wife will be with him, of course, and I've invited his daughter and her husband to make up the numbers,' he explained. 'But of course, you'll have met Jeremy Edwards before, won't you? You worked for Edwards Engineering, didn't you?'

Kate heard the words as if from a great distance. If she had been standing she was sure she would have disgraced herself by collapsing at his feet. To have to meet Jeremy again and act as if there had been nothing between them!

Was she capable of carrying it off, or would her old feelings for him revive when she saw him again? She was aware of Nicholas' voice repeating the question and forced herself to answer normally. 'Yes, I know Jeremy Edwards.' She wondered how he would react if she added, 'I was going to marry him once.' Instead she heard herself asking, panic-stricken, 'Can't Diana organise the dinner party for you?'

'What's the matter? Don't you think you're up to it? Or is it something else?' Nicholas was eyeing her with his usual penetration. Had his shrewd brain already started delving beneath the surface and speculating on the nature of her relationship with Jeremy?

'You've already put her nose out of joint once—twice—this week,' she ventured tentatively, remembering the brief phone conversation that morning.

'She'll get used to it,' he said indifferently. 'I'm not asking her. I'm asking you. Can you imagine Diana being tactful and intelligent? Or either?'

He obviously considered the matter closed and to try to argue further would only make him suspicious about her reasons for dodging a meeting with Sir Geoffrey and his family. Instead she acquiesced and took down all the details necessary for the occasion.

'You've got a week to get organised,' Nicholas told her casually, by way of reassurance.

And to worry herself sick about how Jeremy would react when he saw her again, she thought despondently. Outwardly bright and efficient, she got to her feet and prepared to leave his office.

'Oh, there's one thing——' he checked her.

'Yes?'

'Your dress.' Nicholas eyed her thoughtfully and she felt suddenly self-conscious under his gaze. He might have been buying a slave-girl at an auction from the way he looked at her.

'My dress?' she echoed, puzzled.

'Get yourself something suitable for the party and give me the bill. You needn't stint yourself, I want you to look good.'

'I have a dress which will be perfectly adequate for the occasion, thank you,' she said frostily.

'I don't want you to look adequate. I expect you to dazzle my guests. And, if your present wardrobe's anything to go by,' his expression clearly indicated what he thought of the black dress, 'I hardly think you possess anything suitable.'

'You've obviously got such a low opinion of my dress sense I'm surprised that you trust me to buy something new,' she challenged him. 'Perhaps you'd like to come and choose it with me, then you'd be sure you got your money's worth!'

'I've done that before now,' he murmured wickedly. 'But I'll spare you the embarrassment, Kate. I'm sure I can rely on you to find the right thing.'

'And there's no need for you to buy my dress. You pay me well enough for the—privilege—of working with you. I don't need any money from you.'

'Don't be so damned stubborn,' he told her irritably. 'You're doing a job of work and you need the right tools for it. I don't suppose we'd be arguing if I'd told you to get yourself a new typewriter or an office chair.'

'That's different.'

'You're thinking about your reputation again,' he taunted her.

'What if I am?'

'If you make any more allusions to my expected assault on your virtue you might find yourself taken up on them,' he said, the taut note in his voice warning her that this conversation could move into dangerous channels. 'But if you're so anxious not to take something you haven't earned, I'm sure we could arrange some kind of repayment.' He got to his feet in one lithe movement and came towards her.

'No!' She backed hastily away, only to see from the amused light in his eyes that he had not been serious after all. She never knew quite whether to take him seriously and he was all too well aware of it.

'No more arguments, then?' he said. 'You'll do as I say?'

'I'll do as you say,' she agreed obediently.

His mocking laughter followed her from the room.

She would get her own back on him for winning that little round, Kate vowed, as she set off for Knightsbridge later that week to buy a dress for the dinner party. Nicholas had told her to get something that looked good. She would spend his money on the most expensive dress she could find and it would serve him right. Not that the size of the bill was likely to shock him; she had a shrewd suspicion that Nicholas Blake was well versed in the matter of settling accounts for his lady friends. He would probably regard any bill his secretary chose to run up as just another in a long line of such expenses. And with a bank account like a bottomless pit, thought Kate crudely, he could afford to be generous. Even so her heart missed a beat when, having fixed on a deliciously feminine creation in low-cut flame chiffon, which outlined her perfect figure and provided a vivid contrast to her chestnut hair and eyes, she charged what seemed an astronomical figure to Nicholas Blake's account.

Twirling round the sitting room giving Jane a special preview of the new dress, Kate winced when her flat-mate commented admiringly, 'That should make Jeremy sit up and realise what he missed!'

'Oh, I don't know. I expect a part share in his new father-in-law's business now and the prospect of the whole empire when Sir Geoffrey retires is enough for anyone—even Jeremy,' she said cynically.

'Do I detect a slightly sour note? Has disillusion set in at last?'

'I think I got over Jeremy the day he threw me over for Felicity. It was my pride that took a knock and stopped me forgetting,' Kate replied. 'That doesn't mean tomorrow night won't be incredibly difficult to handle. Meeting him again will be awkward. I don't know whether he'll acknowledge me or pretend I never existed for him. And the fact that Nicholas never misses a trick will make the evening even more difficult to get through.'

'Ah yes, Nicholas. And where does he fit into the scheme of things? Is that gorgeous dress intended to knock him for six?'

'In more ways than one,' said Kate, avoiding her friend's gaze and studying herself critically in the mirror. 'He's paying for it and it cost a small fortune.'

Jane gave a low whistle. 'And what does he get in return?'

'The pleasure of seeing me wear it—no more, no less.'

'That's what you think,' her friend said sceptically. 'Be careful, Kate. That man was charming women in his cradle. He's forgotten more about the seduction game than you've ever learnt.'

'Don't worry, I can handle him.'

'Famous last words! I wonder how many women have said *that* before they met Nicholas Blake. I bet they ate their words afterwards.'

'I can look after myself,' Kate said firmly.

But, two days later, as she stepped out of the lift and stood outside Nicholas' penthouse flat with the suitcase containing her evening clothes in her hand, she felt a mass of nerves. But it was too late to retreat now. She rang the bell firmly and wondered who would answer it. Did Nicholas have a housekeeper or manservant to look after him? She did not know. In fact, apart from the names of the string of lovely ladies who shared his life from time to time, she knew remarkably little about her employer's private life.

He answered the door to her himself wearing a short towelling robe, carelessly belted at the waist, which left little of his broad-shouldered, lean-hipped frame to the imagination. It was all too clear to Kate that he wore nothing underneath it. He was obviously fresh from the shower. His dark hair, normally so severely groomed, sprang away from his face in damp tendrils giving him, if it was possible, a curiously boyish look. The tang of the masculine cologne he used caught at Kate's senses as she stepped past him into the hall.

'I showered early to leave the bathroom free for you,' he explained as he led the way across to the spare room where Kate was to change. 'It's through there and all yours when you need it. My bedroom's next door to it.'

'I'm hardly likely to need that,' she said pointedly, and he gave her a glinting smile.

'You never know when you might change your mind. Nothing you did would surprise me, Kate.' He turned to leave. 'Shout if there's anything you want. When you're ready I'll show you the rest of the flat and the arrangements for dinner. Don't push yourself, we've plenty of time before they're due.'

With that he disappeared, shutting the door behind him. Kate heard him whistling softly as he made his way along the corridor to his own room. Well, at least *he* sounded relaxed enough. That was one problem less to deal with. About her own feelings Kate was less sure. For all her brave words to Jane about having got Jeremy out of her system she was still uncertain of the effect he would have upon her. Was it possible to stop loving a man so quickly? She doubted it somehow. Then she was faced with deciding either that she had never really been in love with Jeremy or that she was fooling herself when she told herself that she had got over him and would respond to him again the moment she saw him. Either solution was equally unpalatable, particularly under the acute gaze of her employer, who would no doubt gain a good deal of pleasure from the situation if he was aware of it.

Left to her own devices, she glanced round the room. It was furnished with taste and offered every expensive luxury including a king-size bed, but it lacked character and gave no indication of use. Presumably it was hardly needed. Kate assumed that the succession of house guests that Nicholas chose to entertain would no doubt *not* be banished to the spare room. She pulled a face at her disapproving reflection in the ornate, full-length mirror. Who Nicholas entertained was none of her business and she should try to remember that fact. Laying her cosmetics on a dressing table surface which would have made three of the one in her minute bedroom at the flat, she donned a dressing gown, picked up her toiletbag and headed cautiously for the bathroom, childishly praying that she would not bump into her employer en route. Nicholas Blake in a formal business suit could shake her senses easily enough, but clad in a towelling robe the effect he had upon her was even more dynamic. Fortunately the corridor was empty and she reached the bathroom and locked the door without encountering him.

There was a curiously intimate feeling about using the shower, still warm and steamy from its last occupant and with the smell of the expensive soap he used lingering in the air. It was almost like being married to him. She caught herself speculating what it would be like to live with Nicholas, to share every part of his life, and shivered deliciously at the thought. It would be heaven and hell combined, she imagined, and caught herself up with a guilty start. She told herself firmly that she was lucky that it was a state that she would never experience.

Stepping from under the warm water, she wrapped a fluffy towel around her and inspected the exclusive body lotions and perfumes which sat, somewhat incongruously, next to more masculine impedimenta on the shelf. Nicholas evidently believed in making his female guests feel at home, she thought with a sudden resentment that she could not explain as she came upon Chanel No 5, the scent which, in Kate's mind, was always associated indelibly with Diana Kendall.

Back in her room again she quickly donned fresh underclothes, carefully made up her face and brushed her hair. Well, she was no beauty, she thought, looking at the result, but she did not think she would disgrace him. He had told her to look good and if he was not satisfied with the result it was his hard luck. She took her dress down from its hanger and stepped carefully into it, pulling it up over her shoulders. Yes, she had been right to give in to the saleswoman's enthusiastic praise and take it: the colour highlighted the glossy chestnut of her hair and gave her face with its high cheekbones and slightly slanting eyes a faintly exotic look which Kate knew suited her. She could never aspire to the full-bodied loveliness of someone like Diana Kendall, but her own brand of attraction pleased her well enough when she surveyed the reflection in the mirror.

She reached behind her to pull up the zip and suddenly groaned as she felt it stick halfway up. Squinting at her back in the mirror she saw that a piece of the delicate material had caught in the fastener. She tugged at it, first tentatively, then with growing desperation, but to no avail. She realised that if she persisted she would only succeed in tearing the dress. There was no help for it, she would have to ask Nicholas to disentangle the problem.

She braced herself and called, 'Mr Blake! Nicholas!' There was no response, which was hardly surprising considering that nervousness strangled the words almost before they were out of her mouth. She sighed and tugged at the zip again, fooling herself that it might miraculously have unstuck itself. There was nothing else she could do except go and find Nicholas.

She forced herself to her feet and out of the room. Outside the door she paused, her nerve nearly letting her down. Then she knocked timidly and, on hearing his 'Come in', she took a deep breath and entered. The room was a sombre setting for its owner, suggesting a serious man rather than a gadabout playboy. The walls and velvet drapes at the window embrasure were in shades of dark brown and the almost oppressive atmosphere was relieved only by the cream carpet into which her feet sank as she took a few steps over the threshold. It was plain and bare of ornaments apart from what appeared to be a genuine Corot on the wall and in complete contrast a solitary, beautifully ornate ivory figurine on a small table by the bed.

Nicholas had not yet donned the jacket of his evening suit. He was standing in his shirt sleeves in front of the mirror, fastening his tie, a task which seemed to require considerable concentration on his part, for it was a second before he wrenched it apart with a muttered exclamation and turned to acknowledge Kate's presence.

'This is an unexpected surprise,' he greeted her. 'I thought you'd sooner cross the gates of Hell than over the unholy threshold of my bedroom.'

The crisp, white shirt emphasised the powerful column of his tanned throat and accentuated his dark good looks. In evening dress he looked impossibly handsome and she was sure that he was well aware of it. Hands on his hips, he regarded her quizzically. 'Did you want something other than the pleasure of watching me dress for dinner?'

'It's my zip,' she explained hastily. 'It seems to have stuck.' She saw the half-smile on his face and wondered how many times he had been waylaid by women using that excuse to invade his bedroom. But in her case it was the pure and simple truth.

'Let me have a look. I'll see what I can do.' He strode over to her and turned her round to inspect the problem. 'Yes, you certainly had a good go at untangling it yourself before you came to ask me for help, didn't you?'

'I didn't want to bother you.'

'Am I such an ogre? No, don't bother to answer that. I've a fair idea what you think of me.'

She ignored the remark and asked anxiously, 'Can you do anything?'

'Keep still.' It was an effort to obey him as the mere touch of his hands on the bare flesh of her back sent trickles of warm sensation down the whole length of her spine. She hoped that he would not notice the effect he had upon her, but was horribly afraid that he would. Nicholas Blake never missed anything where an attractive woman was concerned, and she was no exception.

He took his time over the task, but finally she felt the pull of the zip as he freed it and then ran it up to the top of the dress where he fastened the tiny eyelet which secured it. 'There you are,' he said casually. 'It wasn't worth making such a fuss about, was it?'

'Did I make a fuss?' she asked, all too conscious that his hands were resting lightly on her shoulders, holding her close to him. He seemed uninclined to move away.

'You looked as if the skies had fallen. Was it the prospect of greeting our dinner guests like that that was appalling you or just the thought of asking my help?'

Damn the man! Where she was concerned he was too perceptive by half. She laughed, wishing he would release her. 'You have to admit it would have been a little unconventional to greet Sir Geoffrey half-naked.'

'Oh, I'm sure he would have appreciated it. I certainly did.' She felt his lips brush against the back of her neck and shivered slightly. 'You have a beautiful body, Kate.'

'You're very kind. Coming from a connoisseur such as yourself that's quite a compliment,' she said, attempting to move away from him. But he retained his grasp on her, merely taking the opportunity to turn her round to face him.

'And that dress displays you to the best advantage,' he continued.

'I hope you still approve when you see the bill. I was rather nervous about spending that amount of money, even though you did tell me to get something good.'

'And you're still nervous, aren't you? Are you afraid that I'm going to demand something in return for my services as a valet?'

The sensual, slightly cruel lips were only inches from hers. If he chose to kiss her she was helpless to stop him. And she did not even know if she wanted to. 'Are you?' she asked, raising her head and meeting his gaze defiantly.

'Yes,' he said, pausing slightly to savour the apprehension on her face before he added, 'You can do my tie for me. I was having trouble with it when you came in.'

She felt almost weak at his words—whether with relief or disappointment she could not have said. His eyes never left her face as she fumbled with the dark strips of material, making two attempts before she managed to creditable bow.

'Thank you.' He stepped away from her and viewed the result in the mirror before shrugging himself into his jacket. 'You have hidden talents. I must bear them in mind for the future.'

There was no answer she could safely make to that, so she remained silent.

'If you're ready now, I'll show you round the flat and you can see the caterer about the food,' he said, going to the door and holding it open for her to precede him. Never had she been so glad to leave a room in her life and from the speed at which she moved Kate guessed that he realised it, although the carefully bland expression on his face gave no hint of his thoughts.

He gave her a brisk tour of the other rooms, explaining that they would have aperitifs in the elegantly furnished sitting room before dinner and return there for coffee afterwards. The dining room, its beautiful rosewood table attractively laid with gleaming silver, presented a warmly welcoming picture. In the kitchen Kate was introduced to the girl from the catering firm who had cooked the meal and was to stay to serve it. Everything, it appeared, was well under control.

'So you see there's nothing to worry about.' Nicholas said bracingly as he led her back into the sitting room and poured her a dry sherry to steady her nerves against the prospect of the evening ahead.

'Nothing at all,' she smiled. That was if you did not count the gigantic hurdle of meeting Jeremy again. She supposed that it was a situation that Nicholas would take in his usual cool, confident fashion. Presumably he was accustomed to such matters. London was probably littered with his ex-girl-friends.

'Did you know Edwards well?' he asked her. 'It was only a small firm, so I suppose you had a fair amount of contact with him?'

She was glad now that she had been cautious enough never to mention exactly what she had done at Edwards Engineering. He had never enquired until now and she had been too glad to banish the past from her mind. 'No, not well,' she lied.

'Why *did* you actually leave them?' he was asking curiously, making her heart miss a beat, when the doorbell rang and brought her release. He abandoned the question and moved to greet his guests.

Licking suddenly dry lips, Kate set down her glass and got to her feet, hoping that Nicholas would attribute the unnaturally bright smile that she had pinned on her face to nerves. Then there was no more time to worry about anything.

CHAPTER EIGHT

THE meal was half over before Kate was able to relax her taut nerves and allow herself the luxury of assessing how everything was going. The food so far had been superb—or so their guests had thought at least. They had been loud in their compliments. She herself had barely tasted it: the avocado mousse followed by fish in a piquant sauce could have been sawdust for all she was aware of what she was eating. Yet she could tell that Nicholas was pleased with her; the glance he had given her as they had moved into the dining room had indicated his approval of the way she had handled his guests so far. Not that it had been difficult once the tense initial meeting with Jeremy was over and she had worked out which way he had intended to play it.

She had to admire the coolness with which he had acknowledged her presence at Nicholas' side. He smiled politely and shook her hand as if she had indeed been the casual fellow worker that he pretended to recall. 'Ah, yes, of course I remember Miss Sherwood. You worked for Saunders, didn't you?'

She wondered what would have happened if she had not followed his lead. If she had said sweetly, 'No, that was someone else. I was your fiancée, if you remember. You said we'd get engaged when the Markham deal was over.' *That* would have set the cat among the pigeons. But she could not do it. Her pride would not let her make a scene, as Jeremy knew only too well. Instead she went along with the fiction, giving him a stiff smile which was all she could manage under the circumstances. 'Yes, I worked with Mr Saunders,' she agreed. 'It's good to see you again, *Mr* Edwards.'

The faint stress she laid upon the word brought a quick, searching glance from Nicholas. Not much escaped him. Jeremy had the grace to look slightly taken aback, but recovered swiftly, realising probably that it was hardly in her interest to give herself away and create a scene in front of her new employer's honoured guests. 'Come now, we're all friends together tonight, so don't be formal. I'm Jeremy out of the office, remember?'

'I remember,' she said. Remember? How could she forget? She had hoped to be Mrs Jeremy Edwards once. Now it was the slim, blonde girl, whose looks had a chocolate-box prettiness, whom he drew forward and introduced as his wife, Felicity.

She gave Kate a vapid smile, patently uninterested in a mere secretary, and turned to look adoringly at Nicholas. She might be newly married to Jeremy, but that did not seem to stop her appreciation of another, more attractive man when he came into her sphere. And, looking at the two men standing side by side, Kate could not help agreeing with her. Jeremy's smooth, blond handsomeness seemed pale and insignificant beside Nicholas' dark, forceful features. Although the two men were of an age Jeremy was a boy in experience of the world compared with his host. And the difference showed. Nicholas had not a weak bone in his body. He knew what he wanted and took it, but never in the way that Jeremy had done. *He* would never marry to help himself to business success, of that Kate was sure.

If Nicholas had any thoughts along the same lines he concealed them admirably. Jeremy and his wife might only be present to 'make up the numbers' as he had phrased it to Kate, but he gave no indication of the fact, his face expressing nothing but polite interest in his guests as he chatted casually with them and made every effort to entertain them.

Not that it was difficult to talk to Sir Geoffrey Markham and his wife, thought Kate gratefully, as she left Nicholas to deal with Jeremy and Felicity and went to sit beside the older couple. Their daughter might be a snobbish bitch, but the Markhams themselves were pleasant and genuinely interested in what she had to say. It took only a few minutes to establish that Sir Geoffrey's gruff exterior was only a front to conceal the warm, caring personality underneath. He might be a tough, hard-hitting businessman in the office, she decided, but socially he was charming, and Lady Markham was as unaffected and as easy to talk to as her husband.

'And how do you enjoy working with young Blake?' Sir Geoffrey asked Kate after he had established what her position was in Nicholas' life. 'Never a dull moment, eh?'

She hid a smile at hearing her employer referred to as if he were a bright lad with a promising future instead of the established, highly regarded business brain that he was. 'You could say that,' she said wryly.

'You mustn't let him bully you, my dear,' Lady Markham advised. 'These businessmen are all the same. The only way to deal with them is to stand up to them and take no nonsense from them.'

'And does that method really work?' Kate asked laughingly.

'It hasn't failed me in nearly thirty years of being married to one of the most temperamental specimens of the type that you're ever likely to encounter.' She threw an affectionate glance at her husband as she spoke and Kate could sense the undercurrent of real happiness that flowed between them.

'A wife generally has more control over her husband

than his secretary does,' she pointed out.

'And a good thing too, or the office would take over completely,' Lady Markham said firmly, challenging her husband to disagree.

He smiled, not rising to her bait, and changed the subject adroitly. 'I hear you used to work in my son-in-law's firm, Miss Sherwood?'

'Do please call me Kate.' As she spoke the words pleasantly enough she could feel the tension in the pit of her stomach. Sir Geoffrey had never met her before; Jeremy had kept her firmly out of the way during the negotiations. But did he suspect something? Perhaps it was just an innocent enquiry and she was fussing about nothing. 'Yes,' she said, desperately hoping that her voice sounded unconcerned. 'I moved a few months ago.'

'You wouldn't have done if I'd known about you, young lady,' Sir Geoffrey complimented her with heavy gallantry. 'You'd be an asset to any firm, my dear. I only hope young Blake realises what a prize he's got.'

'He does indeed.' Kate jumped as she heard Nicholas' voice behind her and felt the warm, strangely reassuring pressure of his hands on her shoulders. 'Edwards' loss was certainly my gain.'

Sir Geoffrey laughed. 'Always an eye for an attractive woman, eh? It's time you settled down, stopped playing the field and got married.'

If Nicholas resented the intrusion into his private life he gave no sign of it. 'Oh, I have it in mind,' he said dismissively. 'She hasn't said she'll have me yet.'

'Have you asked her, Nicholas? Be honest!' Lady Markham asked with a smile.

There was an answering glint in his eye. 'Let's say that I'm biding my time.'

'Or putting off the evil moment when you lose your freedom. You men are all the same! It took me two years to get Geoffrey to the altar.'

There was general laughter and the subject was closed. But, as they moved into the dining room for the meal, Kate pondered over what Nicholas had said. It looked as if Diana had won after all and he had decided to marry her at last. She supposed she should feel glad that someone had outmanoeuvred him. He was dictatorial and overbearing and totally arrogant and he deserved every ounce of misery that his union with Diana would bring him. Yet, looking at the dark head bent attentively close to Lady Markham to catch a comment she had made, she knew in her heart that she could never wish Nicholas unhappiness. In that moment she admitted to herself what she supposed she had acknowledged subconsciously all along: that what she felt for him was no mere physical attraction, but love. What she had felt for Jeremy was a pale nothing compared with the way that the very sight of Nicholas set her senses ablaze and made her whole world come alive.

Under cover of refilling her water glass she glanced at Jeremy, seated on her left, who had been careful to address the occasional remark to her rather than drawing attention by ignoring her completely, but who had devoted most of his attention to Felicity. Perhaps he thought it unwise to subject her to too much of her host's charm. It was an understandable fear, thought Kate with faint amusement, for Felicity's features were eye-catching enough and she obviously found Nicholas attractive company. And how could Jeremy's blond, rather insipid good looks compare with his host's dark sensuality? It was strange that she had never noticed Jeremy's weak chin and tight, rather repressive mouth when she had known him. One look at Nicholas revealed his strength of character in every line of his face.

But she had got Jeremy out of her system only to be

faced with an even greater dilemma. How could she go on working for Nicholas knowing how she felt about him? And how could she find an adequate excuse to explain her desire to leave? If she stayed could she bear the torment of working closely with him every day and bottling up her feelings for him? Even now she looked swiftly away from him, scared in case the sudden realisation of her love for him could be read on her face.

He must never know how she felt about him. It had been impossible to conceal her physical response to him; he knew only too well what effect his practised caresses had upon her. But to let him become aware that he possessed her body and soul was to allow him to make her just another of his playthings to be tossed aside when he was no longer amused by her. And how he would revel in the knowledge that she, who had vowed that she was immune, had fallen victim to his charms at last! He might intend to make Diana his wife, but he would be more than prepared to have a fling with his secretary in the meantime, of that she was sure. But a brief affair with him would be as heartbreaking as nothing at all.

She was vaguely aware of Sir Geoffrey at her side asking her a question and brought herself back to the present with a bump.

'The food? Yes, it is good, isn't it? Only a small firm, I understand, but they're beginning to build up a reputation.'

'Good food, good wine and, most important, good company. We've certainly got all three tonight, my dear.' He patted her hand familiarly. 'You must come over with Nicholas to us some time and we'll return the compliment.'

'I'd be delighted to.' Kate smiled brightly at him, while inwardly determining that nothing short of wild horses would drag her to any more social occasions with her employer. She had discovered their pitfalls already.

When the meal was over and even Sir Geoffrey's sweet tooth could not be tempted to another slice of the Black Forest gateau, Kate let Nicholas usher the guests into the sitting room while she went to say a word of congratulation to the girl from the caterers and ask for coffee to be served. When she rejoined the party she was hardly surprised to see that Felicity had secured a seat next to Nicholas on the elegant, black leather sofa which dominated the room and was making a determined effort to monopolise his attention. Fortunately, whether he was conscious of her intention or not, he was far too good a host to ignore any of his guests, and by the time Kate had filled and passed round the coffee cups and dainty petits fours he had drawn the Markham family into a lively discussion of modern art, yet another subject on which, to judge by his comments, he was an expert.

Jeremy sat slightly apart, a rather sulky expression on his face, all too obviously resenting the way in which his wife hung on Nicholas' every word. But he was wise enough to know better than to try to compete. Nicholas was a born story-teller and to listen to his account of how he tracked down a particular work by a favourite artist and persuaded its owner to part with it was to be aware of the power he held over an audience. He could make one think black was white, thought Kate, marvelling.

'That reminds me of a time, years ago, when I had a similar sort of experience——' Sir Geoffrey, with much prompting from his wife, embarked on a longwinded account of one of his triumphs.

Kate smiled as she slipped away to the spare room to powder her shy nose and take a moment's breathing space. Sir Geoffrey was a wonderful old man. She could never imagine anyone being scared of him. But perhaps he, like Nicholas, showed a different side of himself in the office.

She sat down at the dressing table and was making minor repairs to her make-up when a noise at the door made her suddenly aware that she was no longer alone. Startled, she looked behind her to see a male figure lounging against the door post.

'Well, Kate, it's been a long time.'

'Jeremy! What do you want?'

He smiled nastily. 'Just to congratulate you. You've certainly done well for yourself.'

'And what exactly do you mean by that?' she asked.

'You landed on your feet all right with Nicholas Blake to look after you. They tell me he's a generous man to those that—please him.'

'If you're suggesting what I think you are, you're totally wrong.'

'Oh, come on, Kate. Why bother to deny it? I saw the lovey-dovey picture of you out on the town with him the other night.' He straightened up and came towards her, perching on the corner of the dressing table and surveying her with an assessing glance which made her uncomfortably aware of the plunging neckline of her dress. 'You've blossomed quite a lot since you worked for me, haven't you? Of course the clothes do help the sophisticated image. He's got good taste.'

'How dare you!'

'Are you telling me he didn't pay for the dress you're wearing? Come off it, secretaries don't earn enough to swan around in model gowns. I know quality when I see it, and Felicity makes sure I know all too well how much a dress like that costs.'

She opened her mouth to deny the charge, then hesitated. After all, Nicholas *had* bought her dress. 'It's not what you think,' she said desperately, wondering why she bothered to defend herself, but knowing that she had to for the sake of her own self-respect.

'No?' His tone was disbelieving. 'You've certainly changed since I knew you. You're not as prim and proper as you made out, are you? You women make me sick! One word from someone with a lot of money and you fall like ninepins. I suppose I wasn't rich enough for you.'

'As I remember,' she said, trying to keep calm, 'it was you who left me without so much as a by your-leave for the chance to feather your own nest. So don't accuse me of being a gold-digger.'

He shrugged. 'It seemed the obvious thing to do at the time. And Felicity's no fool. She won't expect me to remain faithful to her. It suited her to marry and get away from Daddy's fuddy-duddy ideas. Marriage gave her freedom and it gave me money. Fair exchange.'

'You're despicable!' Kate's temper flared and she flung the words at him.

'No worse than you, my darling. I put money before principles and so did you. We're two of a kind, so why not admit it?'

'I've nothing at all in common with you. God knows what I ever saw in you.'

'You found me attractive. You still do. You expected me to follow you tonight—I saw the look you gave me before you left the room.'

It was useless to maintain that she had done nothing of the sort. His conceit was enormous and, if he still believed that she felt something for him, it was going to be almost impossible to convince him otherwise. 'Look, Jeremy, I'm not interested,' she began firmly, and then got firmly to her feet and backed away as he lunged at her.

'Playing hard to get? You always did that well enough.

And I was fool enough to think you were genuine. But I know better now, don't I?' He moved forward, forcing her to retreat across the room until she felt the hard edge of the bed behind her legs and realised that he had cornered her.

'Jeremy! Please!' She flung her hands against him in a vain effort to stop him moving any nearer, but he thrust them aside and seized her shoulders, pulling her closer to him. She fought desperately, but her struggles seemed only to excite him. Then, as she kicked out against his shins, she lost her balance and collapsed backwards on to the bed with Jeremy on top of her.

She wriggled frantically to escape the passionate kisses which he pressed on her and lashed out in an attempt to discourage the hands which were roving over her bodice, attempting to pull the dress off her shoulders. The heavy weight of his body pinned her down so that she could hardly move and she was aware that his strength was too much for her. She would have screamed, but something at the back of her mind prevented her. What would Felicity think? What would her parents think if they found her with Jeremy like this? And what would Nicholas' reaction be?

She found out sooner than she could imagine for, just as Jeremy's lips left her throat to utter hoarsely, 'Come on, Kate, relax, we're O.K.,' she heard a masculine oath and felt the sudden release from pressure as Jeremy's body was flung from her by a strong, firm hand round the scruff of his neck.

Nicholas stood there breathing heavily, his face dark with fury. 'Just what the hell do you think you're doing?' he demanded.

The question was directed at Jeremy who lay sprawled on the floor where the other man's thrust had pitched him, but Kate had the distinct feeling it was aimed just as much at her. She got up, painfully aware that her dress was wildly disarranged, one shoulder strap slipping off to reveal the signs of Jeremy's passionate lovemaking imprinted on her pale skin.

'Damn you, Blake, why did you have to interrupt?' Jeremy had found his voice.

'Your *wife* was wondering where you'd got to,' Nicholas told him contemptuously. 'I thought you might be up to something like this, so I volunteered to find out.'

'I'd have thought you'd have been too taken up with her to worry about us,' Jeremy sneered. He got to his feet, clearly at a disadvantage with the six foot odd frame of his host standing over him. 'Sauce for the goose is sauce for the gander, particularly with a willing partner available.'

Kate gave a strangled cry, but both men ignored her.

'Oh, she'll tell you a different story, but she was mine a long time before you set eyes on her.'

'Indeed.' Nicholas' voice was level, but a taut nerve moved by his mouth betraying that the gibe had struck home. 'Perhaps you'd like to rejoin your wife and parents-in-law. I don't want them coming looking for you.'

Jeremy shrugged and made for the door. Then he turned and looked back at Kate. 'He's a lot to put up with for the money. I was much more easy-going. But perhaps you've chosen to forget that.'

'Out!' Nicholas ordered, and he went, closing the door behind him.

Shivering with reaction, Kate struggled off the bed and got weakly to her feet. God knows what kind of mess she looked, but, if Nicholas' expression was anything to go by, she was in a bad way.

'Thank you. I thought that he—that he——'

'That he was going to make love to you. That *was* what you wanted, wasn't it? I suppose the fact that his wife was practically next door added spice to everything. And if I hadn't interrupted your cosy little love scene I expect you'd have rejoined the party as if nothing had happened. You little tramp!' The contempt in his voice shook her.

She staggered back and tried to find the words to defend herself. 'You surely can't believe that I engineered *that*?'

'Didn't you?' he asked coldly. 'I hardly think Edwards would force himself on a girl he barely knew before tonight without a pretty good come-on from her.'

She bit her lip. The truth would have to come out now. But would he believe her? 'I did know Jeremy before. We were—close. In fact——'

'Spare me the details,' he said irritably. He looked suddenly weary of the conversation. 'So you were Jeremy Edwards' mistress before you were my secretary. He admitted as much.'

'He was lying,' she said desperately. 'Don't you see, he was just trying to get back at you—at both of us. I was never his mistress. And tonight——'

'Yes?'

'He followed me in here and attacked me.'

'You can do better than that, surely?' He gave a curt laugh.

'It's the truth, I tell you!'

'The way I saw it you were enjoying the experience. I didn't exactly hear any screams of protest.'

'And let his wife discover just what kind of a man Jeremy is? That would have made a fine end to the dinner party,' she told him scathingly.

'And being, as ever, devoted to my interests you were prepared to sacrifice your virtue in the interests of harmony in my business relationships. Very praiseworthy, I'm sure.' The cold sarcasm in his voice told her exactly what he thought of her defence. His ice-grey glance flickered over her, taking in with obvious distaste the state her dress was in. 'Still, as peaceful co-existence with the Markham tribe is so important to both of us, I suggest we salvage the pieces and continue as before. I'd better return to the sitting room or they'll begin to wonder what's going on. Tidy yourself up and join me in a few minutes.'

He was gone before Kate had a chance to say anything more. She sat for a few seconds in numbed silence, willing herself not to shed the hot tears of reaction which pricked behind the back of her eyes. Then, automatically, she straightened her dress and did her best to cover up the fact that just ten short minutes ago she had been fighting as desperate a fight for her virtue as any Victorian maiden might have done. Restored to something like her normal self externally, she took a few deep breaths and tried to control her churning stomach.

How could she possibly go back into the sitting room and face the Markhams as if nothing had happened? But if she did not make the effort they would soon suspect something was wrong. Kate dragged her reluctant limbs to the door and opened it. As she approached the sitting room door and paused hesitantly outside it opened and Nicholas appeared. All trace of the coldly furious man who had confronted her seconds ago had been erased, the polite mask of the good host was on his face. Had it not been for the distant iciness of his hard, grey gaze as it rested upon her she could almost have fooled herself into thinking that the angry words he had thrown at her had never been spoken.

'Ah, there you are, Kate. Sir Geoffrey was all for sending out a search party,' he said with a light laugh. 'I told him you were only prettying yourself for him.'

'I think you're the lucky man,' Sir Geoffrey laughed.

'No girl in her right mind would spare me a second glance with you around. But I'd narrow the odds considerably if I were ten years younger.'

'I'm sure you would have done, Sir Geoffrey.' It was an effort, but somehow she smiled and flirted demurely with him as if completely unaware of Jeremy's figure just to her right, sitting unnaturally upright in one of the deep armchairs.

He leaned forward to contribute to the conversation. Thank goodness he was civilised enough to carry on as if nothing had happened between them. But his words sent a chill through her. 'If the money is right, surely the man himself hardly matters, does he?'

Sir Geoffrey looked slightly taken aback, but Nicholas jumped quickly into the fray. 'Your son-in-law's a cynic —or trying to pretend he's one.' He laughed and Kate marvelled how natural he sounded. 'But I'll not accept that argument from a newly-married man. Particularly not the man who succeeded in carrying off a girl like Felicity.'

Felicity laughed prettily at the compliment and the difficult moment passed. But although Kate talked and laughed as if her life depended upon it, it was hard work and she was relieved when, towards eleven o'clock, Sir Geoffrey announced that they must be going.

'It's been one of the best evenings I've spent in a long while,' he boomed enthusiastically as he wrung Kate's hand at the doorway to the flat. His wife, although less boisterous, was equally lavish with her thanks, compensating for her daughter, who ignored Kate's outstretched hand and her son-in-law who brushed it with his fingers and sprang away quickly as if her touch was red-hot.

Then they were gone and she was left alone with Nicholas. He said nothing after he had slammed the door shut behind their departing guests, but went back into the sitting room. She heard the clink of a glass and, when she followed him slowly to join him there, he was standing by the drinks cabinet pouring himself a generous helping of whisky. He added a squirt of soda and then downed half the contents at a swallow as if he needed it badly. Perhaps he did. It had been quite an evening.

He had shrugged off his jacket and it lay discarded on the floor. Now he put his hand to his neck and wrenched at his tie as if he found it suddenly constricting. She thought he had not registered her presence as she stood nervously by the door, tense and prepared to spring away if he made a sudden movement. Then he glanced briefly in her direction and said with some irritation, 'For God's sake, come in and sit down. I've told you before not to hover in front of me as if you're apologising for your presence.'

She still hesitated, unsure of his mood. Then he drank some more of the whisky and continued, 'Come in, Kate. There's no need to worry. It all went off very well, didn't it? And I can't fault you as a hostess. Possibly you erred a little too far on the side of keeping the guests happy, but I'm splitting hairs, aren't I? After all, the success of the operation depended on giving them what they wanted. Forgive me for not realising that Jeremy Edwards wanted you.' He drained the glass and set it down with a bang.

'I've given you my version of what happened. If you choose not to believe me, that's your fault,' she challenged him, temper getting the better of her nerves as she stepped forward.

'Perhaps you'll be good enough to let me know in future before I invite any of your former lovers to dinner. I'd like to be suitably prepared for anything I may find in the bedroom.'

She rushed at him, her hand raised to slap that cruel, dark face. How dared he insult her like that! 'You——'

He fended her off easily, pinioning her arms behind her back and holding her away from him without apparent effort. 'You little wildcat, you'll play that trick once too often! You can't take the truth, can you, Kate?' he said harshly. 'You're quick enough to make comments about my private life with no proof at all to back them up, but when I actually catch you in bed with a married man I'm supposed not only to disbelieve the evidence of my own eyes, but also to accept the lame explanation you offer me.'

'I was *not* in bed with Jeremy.'

'In bed or on the bed, you certainly seemed as if you were enjoying yourself, and Edwards didn't appear to have any complaints.'

'That's what you think.' Kate writhed impotently in the steel grip. 'I loathe Jeremy Edwards!'

He released her with a look of sudden disgust on his face. 'You expect me to believe that? A fine way you had of showing it. But then you claim to hate me and you come into my arms willingly enough.'

'It's no use trying to convince you,' she said despairingly. 'You won't believe me. You've already judged me, haven't you?'

'Try me.' He crossed to the cabinet again. 'Do you want a drink?'

'No.' It was better to keep her head completely clear.

'Well, I certainly do.' He poured himself another large whisky and sank down on to the sofa, his long legs sprawled out before him. 'Right. I'm eager, ready and willing to be convinced. Start talking.'

She paused, uncertain where to begin, then started baldly, 'I was his secretary. We—I—fell in love. We were going to be married. At least *I* thought so. No one else was surprised when he took off for his honeymoon with Felicity. I was shattered. Do you blame me for getting out and trying to forget?'

He studied the golden liquid in the glass. She could tell nothing of what he was thinking from the blank, shuttered look on his face. 'So you took off for the country?'

'I wanted to sort myself out. Maybe I did get over him then, I don't know. When I got the job with you you didn't ask for references, didn't even seem too interested in what I'd done before I came to you and I was glad to leave it at that. *I* didn't want to rake up the past.'

'What the eye doesn't see the heart doesn't grieve over?'

'You could say that. Perhaps I should have told you when you asked me to help with this evening. I thought I'd got over him and I naturally assumed that as he'd preferred Felicity to me it wouldn't matter to him whether he met me or not.'

'And when you did see him again your feelings got the better of you?' he suggested drily. 'You found it impossible to pack your emotions away.'

'No!' How could she make him understand? 'The moment I saw him again I knew that he meant nothing to me. When he followed me to my room I told him as much—or would have done if he'd let me. Instead he leapt on me. I tried to get away, but couldn't. You know the rest.'

'Yes,' he said, musing.

It was desperately important to make him believe her. She sank to the floor at his feet, gazing imploringly up at him as she pleaded with him to understand. 'I know it looked bad to you, but you *were* mistaken.'

He leant forward suddenly and cupped her head in his hands, forcing her chin up as he looked deep into her eyes. She met the piercing grey gaze unflinchingly. Then he asked abruptly, 'Were you very much in love with him?'

She answered him steadily. 'I was, yes.' There was no need to add that someone else had totally replaced Jeremy in her affections. *That* was a secret that she must keep at all costs.

'There's a remedy for it, you know.'

'Is there?' she asked shakily. The long, firm fingers had moved from beneath her chin and were caressing the soft skin of her neck. She supposed she should get away now while she still could. Every sense of danger suggested it, but she was rooted to the spot, gazing as if hypnotized into the eyes which held her in total thrall.

When he kissed her it was still a shock, although she knew it would happen. The touch of his mouth on hers was warm and infinitely reassuring and she relaxed against him, making no protest when he gathered her up to share the sofa with him. Her arms went round him, her hands sliding over the fine material of his shirt to caress his broad back, glorying in the movement of the strong-muscled body as he pushed her deep into the yielding softness of the cushions and moved to cover her with his body.

'Kate, Kate,' he muttered feverishly as his lips caressed her. She felt the sudden easing of tension as his fingers found and undid the zip of her dress, pulling it away from her shoulders to stroke the creamy flesh of her breasts, revealed above the filmy lace of her bra. He was arousing her to an almost unbearable state of excitement. Her fingers moved to undo the buttons of his shirt, thrusting it aside to explore with sensuous pleasure the contours of the broad chest with its sprinkling of dark hair. What did it matter that tomorrow he would have forgotten the episode? Tonight *she* was the woman in his life and she knew, as if by instinct, how to please and fulfil him.

But what he thought of her did matter despite the ache in her body which told her to ignore other considerations and abandon herself to the ultimate pleasure. When he lifted his lips from hers and told her in a voice thick with desire, 'You're a witch, Kate, did you know that? I'll believe any tale you spin me when you're like this,' a feeling of revulsion at her actions swept over her and her whole body stiffened.

'No, Nicholas, no!' Fighting him, she tried to push him away, her hands clawing desperately at him, raking the flesh of his arms in an effort to make him release her. For a few seconds she thought she had lost the battle, for his grip on her tightened unbearably. Then, with what appeared to be an almost superhuman effort, he tore himself from her and stood, his back turned to her, his shoulders heaving as he took deep breaths to restore his control of himself.

Then he looked back at her where she lay on the sofa, momentarily too shattered to make any effort to get to her feet. His eyes raked her body insolently and then he asked, 'What's the matter? Don't tell me that two men in an evening are too much for you?'

The crudness of his words was like a dash of cold water in her face. She struggled to an upright position, lifting her feet to the ground, although she knew they would not support her if she tried to use them. She could find no words to answer him.

'I shouldn't try that little trick too often. Most men wouldn't be able to cope with your sudden switches of mood.'

'But you're a superman, of course,' Kate threw at him. 'What a wonder you are, to be sure.'

His lip curled. 'At least I've a few more manners than your friend Jeremy. He sulked all evening after he failed to get what he wanted. It's a wonder no one noticed.'

'Whereas you take that sort of thing in your stride, I suppose?'

'Let's say I don't often lose control of myself even when a woman offers herself to me as blatantly as you did tonight and then changes her mind.'

'It must be a new experience for you to find someone who doesn't find you completely irresistible,' she said, fighting to recover from the hurt he had inflicted on her. Her mind would register the cutting insult of his words long after her body had forgotten the pleasure his hands had given her.

His look registered his disbelief of her words. 'Don't fool yourself, Kate. You wanted me all right. I don't pretend to know why you switched off when you did, but I think you'll regret your part in it long before I do.'

He was right, she would regret her actions. Tonight had been probably her only chance to know what it was to find physical fulfilment with the man she loved. But, knowing that she meant nothing to him, there was no way she could have gone through with it. 'You're wrong,' she lied bravely.

'I doubt it,' he said.

She got up and walked unsteadily to the corner of the room where she had left her handbag. There was no more to be said and she felt tired to death. 'I'll get my things. Perhaps you'd get me a taxi home?'

'I'll drive you.'

Her eyes were on the tumbler of whisky that he had taken up again. 'No, thank you.'

He dashed the glass down angrily on the mantelshelf so that a few drops of the liquid splashed against the wall. 'I'm perfectly capable of taking you home.'

'I'm sure you are, but I think we could both use a break from each other's company right now.'

He shrugged. 'You may be right.' He moved to the

telephone. 'I'll get you a cab.'

She went to the bedroom to collect her case, deliberately taking her time to avoid having to sit with him while she waited for the taxi to arrive. When she heard the ring at the door bell a few minutes later she breathed a sigh of relief. On her way to leave she pushed briefly at the sitting room door.

Nicholas was sitting, staring in front of him, his shoulders slumped in a curiously defeated attitude. For once the outer shell had cracked and she was seeing the real man underneath, a man who, for all his strength, was capable of hurt and as vulnerable as anyone else. But had her rejection of him hit at anything more than his pride?

'Goodnight, Nicholas,' she managed to say.

He straightened and turned to her. The grey eyes raked her figure lazily. 'Sweet dreams in that virgin bed of yours, Kate,' he said, and raised his glass to her in a mock toast. As she turned to go he pulled the whisky bottle nearer to him and she heard the sound of the glass being refilled. There was no more to be said tonight. Perhaps there would never be anything more said between them. Without another word she left him.

CHAPTER NINE

NEXT day as she set off for the office Kate blanked her mind to the events of the previous evening. She had spent a restless night turning over and analysing every word, every look that Nicholas had directed at her, and she had to admit she was none the wiser as to what he really thought and why he had acted the way he had. With another man she might have put his violent reaction to the sight of her in Jeremy's arms, supposedly enjoying his kisses, as jealousy, but that could hardly be the case. Disgust at the morals of a woman who went after a married man? It was possible, but unlikely, for Nicholas was no saint himself and in any case was barely concerned with the private lives of his staff. There seemed to be no solution, and as it was hardly likely that the man himself intended to supply one she supposed the best thing to do was to leave the matter alone and hope that everything would blow over.

Nicholas was nowhere to be seen when she opened her office door, and she was faintly relieved. At least she would have the chance to pitch into some work before she encountered him. She might even manage to meet him with some semblance of normality. She began to open the post, keeping a weather eye on the door through which her employer would enter.

As luck would have it he arrived just as she was querying delivery of a large bouquet of flowers.

'No mistake, miss, here's the card with your name on it.' The boy thrust the square of cardboard at her and departed, whistling cheerfully, leaving Kate staring down at the message which read, 'Thank you for a delightful evening—Jeremy.'

Fury blinded her to anything else and she made no resistance when Nicholas reached for the card and read it. 'Not terribly original,' he commented, 'but then that's hardly Edwards' line.'

'Or yours either,' she retorted, taking notice of him for the first time. 'I shall send the flowers back.'

'Fine words, with the delivery boy halfway to his next call.'

She picked up the flowers and rammed them, heads down, into the wastepaper basket. 'Perhaps that'll convince you that I'm not interested in Jeremy Edwards or his flowers.'

'Empty gestures rarely impress me,' he said coldly, turning to the door of his office. 'Besides, it's not me you have to convince, is it? It's yourself.' With that he disappeared and slammed the door behind him.

A night's sleep did not seem to have done him much good either, Kate reflected as she tore Jeremy's card across and added it to the mess in the wastepaper basket. If indeed Nicholas had had any sleep. Although he was his usual immaculate self, there was a tired, drawn look to his face as if he had stayed up too late with only the whisky bottle for company. She wondered if he would bite her head off if she suggested black coffee and decided to make it for him anyway. At least it would show that she at least was not sulking after last night. She took in the coffee pot and a cup and saucer and retreated as noiselessly as she had come when he gave her only a curt 'Thank you' for her trouble.

The phone rang as she returned to her office, and she picked it up and gave her name.

'Did you get the flowers?'

It was Jeremy. Kate suppressed her first instinct to slam down the receiver. He would only ring again if she did. 'Yes, and they've gone straight in the wastepaper basket along with the snide comment that you sent with them.'

'But——'

'Get this clear once and for all, Jeremy Edwards. I was fool enough to fall for you once, but I never make the same mistake twice, particularly not with men like you. I don't know what the idea was in sending me flowers, but whatever it was, it didn't work.'

'It got us talking again.' The self-congratulation in his tone was almost more than she could bear. 'Calm down, Kate. Be reasonable.'

'I'm perfectly reasonable!' She bit the words out. Behind her she heard Nicholas' door open and a prickle running the length of her spine warned her of his presence only inches away from her. 'And I've better things to do with my time than waste it on you. Once and for all, Jeremy, I'm not interested in you. Save the sweet talk for your wife!' Without waiting to hear his reply she slammed the phone down on its rest and turned, her cheeks flushed with temper, to confront the major problems in her life.

Why did he have to set her senses afire every time she saw him? Even after what had obviously been a hard night his vibrant air of male attraction caught and held her a subject to his will. She fought against the magnetic pull as she met his cool gaze and launched into speech out of pure self-defence.

'Do you have to listen to private conversations?'

'Do you have to take private phone calls at the office? If you're going to have tiffs with your lovers, I suggest you keep them for outside office hours,' he told her. 'I pay you to work for me between nine and five. After that your time's your own.'

'I'll remember that in future. And for your information, I was *not* having a tiff, as you call it, with Jeremy. I was telling him to get lost for good and leave me alone.'

'Can't stand the pace, I suppose?' He laughed harshly and the sound jarred on her ears. 'Do what the hell you like. As you're fond of reminding me, it's no concern of mine. But do it outside office hours in future.'

There was no point in arguing with him. 'Yes, *Mr* Blake,' she said through gritted teeth.

If he noted the challenge in her tone he nevertheless ignored it and, the subject closed, reverted to business. 'Get me Mr Cox's file, will you? I'm seeing him today.' She found it and handed it to him without a word and he walked back to his room. At the door he turned again and instructed her casually, 'Oh, ring Miss Kendall, would you, and tell her I'll pick her up at seven tonight?' Without waiting for a response he went into his office and the door closed behind him like a slap in the face for Kate.

'Yes, sir. No, sir. Three bags full, sir,' she muttered viciously to herself as she banged the receiver down after completing his instructions. He had done it on purpose, of course, just to demonstrate that while *she* was clearly incapable of managing her private life and keeping it nicely separated from her business life, *he* could manage it with ease and fully intended to continue doing so. As she went about her work that morning she felt as if she had never hated anyone with as much concentrated loathing as Nicholas Blake.

He remained closeted in his room for the rest of the day and she was not sorry to leave at five o'clock without seeing him again. Perhaps by tomorrow they might both have cooled down slightly and normal relations could be resumed. But somehow she doubted it. She and Nicholas Blake seemed to be on a collision course which could lead only to further and more acrimonious clashes of personality. And the fact that she loved him one moment and hated him the next helped her not the slightest.

Nicholas might have been out on the town with Diana, but it seemed to have done little to restore his temper. Next morning when she entered his office in response to his buzzer, pencil and notebook in hand, he looked distinctly disagreeable. Perhaps Diana had at last indicated her disapproval of being picked up and put down when he felt like it. Kate fervently hoped so.

Whatever he had been working on, it did not look as if he had been successful. Screwed-up balls of paper lay scattered on the floor, papers were in a wild state of confusion instead of their generally orderly piles on his desk and Nicholas, his dark hair tousled as if he had been raking through it with his hands, was considerably less than his usual calm, decisive self.

He began to dictate a letter, then, after several false starts, broke off and impatiently wrenched his tie away from his neck as if he found it constricting. He got up from behind the desk and, thrusting aside the chair, strode to the window where he paced moodily up and down, staring at the scene outside like an animal confined to a cage. Kate watched him silently, not daring to interrupt him in such an uncertain mood, and just hoping that she would be able to get out of the room unscathed. It seemed more than likely that he would vent his temper on her.

He stopped suddenly, apparently coming to a decision of some kind. He turned to her. 'Enough's enough. I'm not in the mood for work today. Have I any appointments?'

Startled at this uncharacteristic behaviour from someone that she would normally have thought of as almost a workaholic until now, Kate took a second or two to recall his engagements for the day. 'A couple. Nothing urgent.'

'Put them off,' he instructed her, and followed her into her office, standing by her side while she picked up the phone and did so.

'All settled,' she told him a few minutes later, and waited to be informed of his further plans for the day.

'Good. What I need is some fresh air.'

She supposed she was tempting him to bite her head off, but asked the question anyway. 'An overdose of stuffy nightclubs?' she enquired sweetly.

'An overdose of foolish women, and one in particular.' He eyed her sourly.

Had he taken the plunge and asked Diana to marry him last night? Surely she could not have refused him if he had done? Or had she accepted him and his temper was the natural reaction of a bachelor who had finally allowed the shackles to be put on him and intended to be led to the altar? Something had caused his unpredictable behaviour this morning, but there was no way of knowing what it was. At least she could restore her own shattered feelings in the peaceful atmosphere of the office with her employer elsewhere.

But it seemed that that was not to be her lot. Nicholas picked up her coat from the stand and thrust it at her. 'Put it on,' he said. 'You're coming with me.'

'But——' The unexpectedness of his words left her at a loss for an answer.

'That's an order, not an invitation, so don't make any excuses.'

He swept her along at his side, one powerful hand under her elbow, almost as if he expected her to take to her heels and run to escape the ordeal of spending the day with him. In spite of herself she could not control the quiver that ran through her at his touch. Her head could never control her senses where Nicholas was concerned; there was no way she could resist the physical thrill his presence gave her.

She was safely installed in the passenger seat of the Porsche and they had left the traffic-packed City streets behind before he deigned to speak to her. 'You're very trusting to let me kidnap you.'

'I didn't have much to say in the matter, did I?' she retorted. 'I suppose you'd have slung me over your shoulder and carried me off bodily if I'd complained.'

'Something like that.' He laughed with genuine amusement and she relaxed slightly. 'Are you scared?'

'No,' she said composedly. 'I've survived you in your worst moods. I suppose I'll come through this one. I'm just surprised that you bothered to bring me along when you obviously class me as one of the foolish women you've decided you dislike so much.'

'Not foolish, Kate,' he corrected her. 'Pigheaded, stubborn, quick-tempered and many other things besides, but I'd never call you foolish.'

You could hardly call that a compliment, Kate thought, yet her heart leapt at his words as if he had handed her a bouquet. 'I'm glad to hear that I have so many of your own sterling qualities,' she said lightly.

'Like attracts like. A few clashes are inevitable.'

Was that how he saw the row that they had had over Jeremy after the dinner party? she wondered. But she knew better than to remind him about *that* subject. Nicholas' ill humour seemed to be fading with every mile that passed, but of all things calculated to bring it back in full force she knew instinctively that Jeremy's name was the likeliest to set off another explosion.

She changed the subject swiftly. 'I don't object to being whisked out of the office, but I would like to know where I'm going.'

'It'll take just over an hour to the coast. We'll stop for lunch on the way. Will that suit you?'

'Fine.' She was slightly amused that it occurred to him to consult her for once.

His eyes were on the road ahead, his strong hands superbly competent at the wheel, but he had registered her reaction and there was a hint of devilry in his smile as he said by way of explanation, 'Long experience of female shilly-shallying has decided me to make up my mind for both of us when I'm out with a woman. Take it as a compliment that I offered you the choice.'

'And dared me to challenge it?'

'Knowing your fondness for opposing me just about every time you open your mouth I'm surprised you didn't.'

She laughed and refused to rise to his baiting.

'Well, am I forgiven?' he asked.

'For what?'

'Behaving like a bear with a sore head for the last two days. My only excuse is that I felt like one.'

If it was intended as an apology she had heard better. But Nicholas Blake was not the sort of man to apologise for his actions. It was a statement of fact and she could take it or leave it. 'Let's forget the last few days,' she said.

'If you like.' And the subject was closed, although the awareness of what had happened during and after the dinner party lay uneasily between them for a while, constricting conversation.

Then, imperceptibly, Kate relaxed again. Nicholas, with his black mood thrown off and determined to charm her, was an entertaining companion as they lunched in a small country pub on sandwiches and apple pie with cream, washed down by draughts of cider. When they set off again it was hard to recall that there had ever been any uneasiness between them as they chatted happily about every subject under the sun. Kate discovered they both had a passion for classical music, a dislike of modern novels and a love of travelling, although whereas Nicholas had covered almost all the world in his trips abroad, her journeys had been strictly the armchair kind. It was interesting to find out more about the private Nicholas Blake, so different from the cool, slightly detached business brain of the office. The time flashed by in his company and she came to with a start when they reached the small coast town which was their destination.

Nicholas parked the car and they made for the beach, deserted so early in the season, for although the pale spring sun shone brightly enough, a keen wind blew gustily in their faces as they walked along. The air was fresh and salty, bracing after the petrol fumes of London, and Kate drew in great gulps of it, delighting in it all.

'Enjoying yourself?' They had stopped to look out to sea where some brightly-painted fishing boats were already taking advantage of the incoming tide. He put his arm casually round her shoulders and she did not move away.

'Yes.' Why should she deny it? A stolen day in his company was bliss, even more precious because it would never happen again. No doubt Diana would see to that. She turned and smiled up at him.

'It's the first time in months I've taken a day off.'

'You should do it more often,' she said, giving way to the impulse to order him about. 'You don't relax enough.'

'Oh? I thought you were the one who accused me of wasting too much time on the pursuit of pleasure?'

She laughed. 'Isn't this better than a stuffy nightclub?'

'Yes.' He was studying her, not the scenery, and she

knew it. 'And the company's better too.'

She moved abruptly away from him, but he followed her, frowning. 'What's the matter?'

She thrust her hands deep into the pockets of her coat and turned to face him. 'Nothing. It's just that there's no need to flirt with me. I'm not one of your girl-friends, remember?'

'I'm well aware of that.' His hands moved out to grasp her and held her facing him, unable to escape his scrutiny. He studied her closely for a while, almost as if memorising her features. 'You're not like any girl I've ever known,' he said, suddenly serious.

Kate gave a shaky laugh, knowing she could not take much more of this. 'Oh, I know I'm not beautiful.'

'As if that mattered!'

But it did matter to him, she thought. He liked his women beautiful, not brainy. He preferred pretty dolls prepared to adore him blindly and not a girl whose best feature was a pair of dark brown eyes and who had a tendency to answer him back. What chance would she stand against any one of them? What hope could there be when Diana had scooped the field?

'I thought most men liked beautiful women,' she said lightly.

'Most men do.' He pulled her closer to him. 'When it suits me, though, I'm capable of looking beneath the surface.'

'Meaning?'

'It takes more to really attract me than conventional good looks, although I admit I appreciate beauty as much as any man.'

She could well endorse that statement! Although what he saw in Diana beyond her pretty face, she could not tell. 'So?' she asked him.

'There's passion underneath that layer of ice that you

like to assume when I'm around. Don't bother to deny it, Kate. I can tell from the way you've responded to me on the occasions when you've let your guard slip.'

She was slightly breathless with the heady sensation of being near him, held against that hard, masculine body and conscious of no desire to break free of him. Her brain told her she was heading for certain disaster if she stayed in his arms, but there was no way she could tear herself away from him. 'You're an attractive man, I'll admit it. I can imagine there are very few women who wouldn't respond to you physically if you looked their way.'

'And that's all.'

'That's all,' she said firmly. Did he really expect her to give him the satisfaction of hearing her say that she loved him? What kind of fool would she make of herself if she did?

The grey eyes searched her face and she looked away, scared that he might read the truth there. 'So you won't take it any further?'

'Become your mistress! Is that what you mean?' She was angry now, the high colour rising in her cheeks as she turned to him again. 'What's the matter, Nicholas? Can't you bear the thought of letting a woman get away without sharing your bed?'

His lips compressed tightly and she could see that her blow had struck home. There was a white, angry look about him and his eyes were as icy cold as the grey Arctic Ocean. 'You don't know what you're turning down.'

'Your opinion of yourself really is boundless, isn't it?' she flashed at him, pushing him away from her with one quick movement and stepping back. The wind flicked her hair in her eyes and she tossed it impatiently aside. 'I'm not interested, can't you see that.'

'You prefer Jeremy Edwards, I suppose?'

'I didn't say that.'

'You didn't need to.' He sounded contemptuous. 'Oh, he's good-looking and rich, I'll grant you that. But I thought you were different in that respect. I thought you'd have wanted a bit more than that. Are you really happy to have a hole-and-corner affair with him?'

'It's none of your business,' she flared.

'He'll never marry you, you know. He may want you, but he'll never lose his head over you. He's got his eye on Markham's empire and he'll get it if he's still married to Felicity when Markham retires. The old man is a strong believer in family tradition. He's no son to leave in charge, so your Jeremy will get the lot. And if you think you mean more to him than the business, you've got a shock coming, my dear.'

The lash of his tongue sickened her. She could listen to no more of his accusations. She turned and ran blindly across the shore, aware of nothing but a desire to get away from the sound of that coldly condemning voice.

'Kate! Kate!' She heard him call her and then the sound of his footsteps in pursuit. She redoubled her efforts, but heard him gaining on her with every second. She did not dare to think what he would do to her when he caught up with her. Her breath coming in gasps, she staggered on. Then, suddenly clumsy in her desperation to get away, she slipped on a loose stone and fell heavily, hitting the ground with a bump that shook her.

'Are you all right?' The anger in his face was briefly replaced by concern for her. When she nodded and, wincing slightly, got to her feet, the anger returned. 'You little fool! You could have hurt yourself pounding across the shingle like that. What do you suppose I would have done if you'd sprained your ankle or worse?'

'I expect you'd have coped. You usually do,' she said

flippantly, past caring what his reaction might be. She had taken all that his temper could throw at her, there was no more that she could suffer.

But there she was wrong. Before she could spring away from him his arms snaked out and pulled her roughly to him. 'Damn you, Kate,' he muttered as his mouth closed over hers in a punishing kiss.

He did not mean her to enjoy the experience, and she did not. There was no gentleness or kindness in the gesture, merely a desire to take his revenge on her for all the trouble she had caused him. The steel grip of his arms around her did not relax until finally he raised his lips from her bruised mouth and in a sudden movement of self-disgust, thrust her away from him. 'Don't act like that again or you've had a foretaste of what'll happen to you,' he told her roughly.

'Perhaps you'd like to leave me alone in future and remember that my private life is nothing to do with you!'

'I'll be glad to.'

There seemed no point in staying any longer. In silence they made their way back to the car and got in. As they headed back to London Kate sat gazing unseeingly out of the window, praying that she would not disgrace herself by bursting into tears. Nicholas concentrated on his driving, never sparing her a glance. As far as he was concerned she might never have existed.

He knew the way to her flat so there was no need to give him directions. She wondered if he would let her get out of the car, still without speaking a word. She was not sure if she was capable of answering him if he did say something. But, as he swung the car round into the tree-lined road where her flat was situated, he broke the silence.

'I suggest we draw a veil over this afternoon's proceedings and, in future, that we attempt to keep our relationship on a purely business level.'

It had not been her that had introduced the personal element, but she did not feel inclined to start another slanging match by telling him so. Instead all she could manage was a stifled, 'Yes,' and she fumbled for the catch that opened the door.

'Here, let me,' he said impatiently. He reached over and his hand brushed hers as he found the lever and pressed it down. She recoiled at his touch and from the sardonic smile he gave she knew that he had noticed it. How nice to be Nicholas Blake and to be invulnerable to hurt and upset. She got out of the car and walked to her door, managing a breathless 'Goodnight' that she was sure he had not heard. Strangely he seemed in no hurry to get away.

Then, as she put the key in the lock and turned it, she heard him call her again and retraced her steps to the car.

'Yes?'

He looked almost as if he regretted recalling her. 'Kate, about Edwards——'

'Well?' She made her tone as chilly as she could, but he was undeterred.

'He's no good for you.'

'That's my affair.'

'I could give him a hint to keep away. There'd be no unpleasantness.' He might have been discussing a business deal from the lack of emotion in his face. 'There are ways of doing these things.'

'I can imagine. You mean you'd tell him to keep away from your property.'

'Something like that.'

'No, thank you.' She wondered how she would have felt if she had been really involved with Jeremy, not just using him as a front to keep face with Nicholas. 'I can look after myself.'

'Can you?' he queried. 'You didn't seem to be managing too well the other night.'

'Goodnight, Nicholas.' She turned and went indoors. It was some time before, leaning against the front door, her legs too weak to carry her into the living room, she finally heard his car start up and drive away.

CHAPTER TEN

AN uneasy peace existed in the office for the rest of the week. Nicholas was cool and detached with the air of polite reserve that had so irritated Kate when she first started working for him. Although she supposed that that was easier to deal with than the passionate lovemaking to which he had subjected her in the weeks since. She responded in kind, speaking to him with a bright politeness of which she was proud.

The sting of his words on that dreadful day by the sea was still with her. When she lay in bed at night she could recall every sentence he had spoken to her on that day and her cheeks flamed in the darkness as she went over them again, tossing sleeplessly as she relived it. If the dark shadows under her eyes betrayed her worried state to Nicholas he showed no awareness of it and continued to pile her with work and expect it completed in double quick time.

'It's a relief in a way,' Kate confessed to Jane. 'I don't have time to think or brood too much.'

'The man's a slave-driver,' her friend said furiously. 'He's exploiting you.'

'Rubbish.' She passed her hand wearily across her forehead. 'He pays me well enough for everything. And I'd rather work myself to a frazzle in his office than earn my keep in his bed.'

'I'm not too sure of that.' Jane had a keen eye and a way of filling in the gaps that Kate had left unfilled when she had repeated the story of her latest contretemps with Nicholas Blake. 'Come on, Kate, you can tell me. You love him, don't you? You must do, or you'd have left him a long time ago and found another job.'

'Jobs aren't that easy to find.'

'That's not true and you know it.'

Kate gave up trying to cover up the situation. 'Oh, what's the use? Yes, I love him, and a fat lot of good that'll do me sitting in his office tearing my heart out for him. But I can't leave him. It's impossible. I've got to see him. Even if he does treat me like an office machine these days, I still can't bear to go.'

'Does he have a clue how you feel about him?' Jane asked.

'No, and he never will. He—he asked me to become his mistress, but I turned him down. I let him think it was still Jeremy that I was interested in.'

'But why, Kate, if you love him?' Jane's attitude to love and marriage was considerably more practical than that of her friend. If marriage was an impossibility for some reason that was no excuse for letting the man in question fade from the picture.

Kate shrugged. 'I'm stupid, I know. I want the lot, don't I?' She smiled bitterly. 'I'm a fool, Jane, but even though I love him I'm not prepared to go to bed with him unless I know that he loves me too. I don't want to be the latest girl in his bed. I don't want to stand by smiling bravely while he marries someone else who can offer him more than I can. I want respect and——'

'In a word, you want him to forsake all others and marry you. It's a nice dream, love, but you're living in Cloud Cuckoo Land.'

'I know. You needn't tell me that. I'm eating my heart out for him and he's still enjoying himself playing the field. Pathetic, isn't it?'

'He's taken up with Diana again?' Jane queried.

'No, she's away in the Bahamas with her parents. But

she'll be back and restored to favour.'

'She must be fairly sure of herself to go off and leave him.'

'She is,' said Kate flatly.

Nicholas had already disappeared for an appointment in the City when she arrived at the offic the next day, but he was due to return for a meeting with Sir Geoffrey Markham at eleven. As the hands of the clock approached that time Kate frowned. It was unlike him to be delayed, but if he did not arrive soon it looked as if she would have to placate Sir Geoffrey, notoriously punctual himself and intolerant of lateness in others. Still, it would be nice to see him again. Apart from the warm letter she had received from his wife thanking her for the evening they had spent with her she had not heard anything from them since the night she referred to mentally as the 'Disastrous Dinner Party'.

There was a knock at the door and she got hastily to her feet. That would be Sir Geoffrey now. He often dispensed with formalities and made his own way up to their floor, according to Nicholas. She gathered it had its inconvenient side sometimes. But her bright smile faded when, in response to her 'come in', Jeremy entered the room.

'What—what are you doing here?' she asked, startled. 'We were expecting Sir Geoffrey.'

'He's laid low with that 'flu bug that's going the rounds. He refused to give in to it, of course, so now he's twice as bad and confined to bed and not allowed up. I'm instructed to take over the meeting with Blake this morning. I suppose I should have rung you to check it would be all right, but knowing your dear boss's opinion of me I thought it was quite likely that if I did he'd decide not to see me. Now that I'm here he can hardly do that. It wouldn't have gone down at all well with father-in-law to go crawling back to him and admit that I hadn't been granted an audience.'

She was beginning to recover slightly from the shock of seeing him again and was able to ask quite calmly, 'Why doesn't Nicholas like you?'

He gave her a knowing look. 'I wouldn't have thought *you'd* have needed to ask that!'

'What do you mean?'

He laughed. 'No need to be unpleasant about it with me. I know.'

'What exactly do you know?'

He looked surprised. 'You hardly thought you'd keep it a secret, did you, with him acting the way he did? He warned me off you in no uncertain terms. He bumped into me a few days ago by design rather than accident, I fancy, and told me to keep away from you in future.'

'Oh, did he indeed!' Kate's eyes flashed with temper.

'And rather forceful he was about it,' said Jeremy, obviously recalling a moment that he had not particularly enjoyed by the look on his face. 'He said he'd see my name stank from one end of the City to the other if I as much as approached you again. And he wasn't joking, I can tell you.'

'So like a good little boy you promised to do as you were told?' she commented, irrationally annoyed by the thought even though she would not thank Jeremy to come anywhere near her.

He looked uncomfortable. 'Kate, you know how it is,' he began uneasily. 'I have to——'

'Only too well. Oh, it's all right, Jeremy, don't worry,' she said coolly. '*I* wouldn't touch you with a bargepole. I just wondered if *you* were man enough to stand on your own feet to get something you wanted in spite of the opposition. I should have realised long ago that you weren't. It would have saved a lot of heartache, wouldn't it?'

'Kate——' he pleaded, and put his hand on her arm, 'I never meant to hurt you. It was just that——'

The door opened behind him and Nicholas walked in. At the sight of Jeremy who let go of Kate as if he had touched a hot brick, he gave a thunderous frown. Jeremy seemed disinclined to say anything in his own defence, so she was forced to explain his presence. 'Jeremy is here as a substitute for Sir Geoffrey,' she said hastily. 'He's down with 'flu and in bed——'

'I'm well aware of that,' Nicholas interrupted her. 'I've just been speaking with his secretary. I explained that in no circumstances will I deal with his son-in-law. I'll wait until Sir Geoffrey is better.' He strode towards his office. 'I'll give you three seconds to get out, Edwards. If you're still here by then it will give me the greatest pleasure in the world to throw you out of my offices.'

But there was no need. Jeremy went instantly, in such haste that he left his briefcase behind him. Kate picked it up and went to run after him, but Nicholas stopped her. 'Send someone round to his office with it later.' His gaze flickered over her with an expression she could not read and she wondered if she was to be the new subject of attack. In that case she had better get her own complaint in first.

'You told Jeremy to stay away from me,' she accused him.

He leaned casually against the door of his office, meeting her gaze levelly. 'Yes, I did,' he admitted.

'Might I ask why you chose to meddle in my affairs?' she demanded. 'I told you to leave it alone.'

He shrugged. 'You obviously weren't capable of coping with him yourself. He was wrong for you, Kate.'

'I'll decide that for myself, thank you!'

'I rather think the decision's been made for you. He knows if he gets across me no amount of pushing from Sir Geoffrey will help his future career.'

'You'd break him?'

'Just like that.' His voice was icily calm and she knew he meant what he said.

'How dare you!' she exclaimed and, hardly knowing what she was doing, her hand shot out and she slapped him hard across the face.

As soon as she had done it she knew that she had made a mistake. He straightened up and stood there, the red imprint of her hand clearly visible on his cheek. For a moment she wondered if he would retaliate, but stood her ground bravely. Then, without a word, he turned and went into his office, shutting the door behind him.

That was it; the final straw. Kate knew that something inside her had snapped at last. She could not take any more of this. She must get away from this office and from the cold, uncaring man who ran it. Almost automatically she crossed to her typewriter and sat down, inserting a sheet of paper in it. Determinedly she typed out a letter of resignation. When she had finished, she read it through and signed it. Then, with a defiant toss of her head, she knocked on his door and went in.

He was standing in his favourite place in front of the window, watching the traffic scuttle along the streets so many hundreds of feet below. Yet she had the curious impression that he was not seeing any of it.

'Last time I gave you this you tore it up,' she said, going up to him and thrusting the letter into his hand. 'This time I don't care what you do with it, but I'm going anyway, so you needn't try to stop me. I've had enough of working with you, Nicholas Blake, and the sooner I leave the better.'

He said nothing, merely opened the envelope and

scanned the contents of the letter. His face revealed little beyond an irritation at being disturbed and did not change after he had read her politely worded request to leave his employment. She had given no reason for wanting to go and hardly needed to. They both knew why it was impossible for her to remain.

'All right. You can go.' His voice was cool and indifferent. He might have been giving her the morning off to go to the dentist's.

She was stunned for a moment. She had half expected him to forbid her to leave, to argue with her, to do anything except take the news so calmly. 'I'll work out my week's notice, of course.'

'There's no need. You'd better go now, this morning.'

'But the work——'

'I'll find someone.' The grey eyes were cold as they rested briefly on her. 'I managed before you came and I'll manage again.'

As she left the room he had resumed his position in front of the window, his face expressionless. If she had expected anything else from him she was doomed to disappointment.

It did not take her long to empty the drawers of her desk of her personal possessions. After all, she had hardly been there long enough to accumulate a vast stock of treasures. With everything gathered together she got her coat and put it on. Then she glanced across at the door to Nicholas' room. Should she go and say goodbye? He would not care either way, she supposed, but it might look churlish if she omitted to do it. She crossed the room swiftly and knocked.

His 'Come in' sounded slightly irritable, but she entered nonetheless. He was sitting at his desk, apparently deep in some document, his head bent intently over it. 'Yes?' he said without looking up.

'I came to say goodbye,' she faltered.

At that he glanced up at her. 'Goodbye, Kate,' he said. 'It's certainly been an experience working with you.'

She did not miss the slight irony in his tone. 'I've enjoyed it,' she told him, not entirely truthfully.

'If you need a reference for your next job, I'll be happy to supply one.'

'Thank you.' Suddenly her eyes were swimming with tears. His figure blurred as she looked at him. She blinked quickly. She must get out of his room without making a fool of herself. 'Well, goodbye,' she said hastily, and backed to the door. She could not have borne to have shaken hands with him and was glad that it did not seem to have occurred to him. In the outer office she picked up her things and almost ran for the lift. Once outside the building she walked firmly away, refusing to look round for the last glimpse of his office window. Damn Nicholas Blake, she told herself angrily, knowing all the time that she did not mean it.

When Jane arrived home from work she dispensed coffee and sympathy after learning of Kate's action. 'You've done the right thing there, love,' she counselled. 'You didn't expect him to go down on his bended knees and beg you to stay, did you?'

'Well, no, but——'

'But nothing. Men are all stinkers, even the best of them,' her friend told her firmly. 'Out of sight and out of mind. You'll soon forget him when you've got another job.'

If she lived to be a hundred she did not think she would forget Nicholas Blake, but she did not say so, merely falling in with all Jane's efforts to cheer her up. 'Yes, you're right. At least another job will keep my mind off him.'

Jane frowned. 'You look awful,' she said with the candour of a true friend. 'In your present state you're not going to convince anyone you're the greatest secretary out. You need a few days' rest before you try anything.'

And so, by dint of Jane's urging and her own feeling that she did not care if she never had a job ever again, Kate decided to postpone the job hunt for a week and to go back to Aunt Meg for another stay.

'It won't do any good, you know,' she told Jane in response to the other's bracing talk of how much brighter she would be for the country air and Aunt Meg's home-cooked food. 'After all, look what happened last time I went there for a rest-cure.'

'Lightning never strikes twice in the same place,' her friend said firmly, waving her goodbye. 'I'll give you three days and you'll have forgotten him completely.'

'Fat chance,' said Kate, and meant it, but she laughed for the first time in days.

If Aunt Meg was concerned by the pallor of Kate's face and the dark shadows under her eyes she was tactful enough not to mention it, merely welcoming her adopted niece with her usual warmth and promising her the delights of country cooking. 'That's what brings the visitors back year after year,' she told Kate. 'A taste of my homemade bread and they're ruined for shop-bought rubbish in the future.'

She was right, Kate had to admit. Although she had little appetite when she arrived, a few days of long walks in the Cotswold countryside, now putting forward its spring greenery, brought colour to her cheeks and a growing taste for the food which Aunt Meg pressed on her with a lavish hand.

'I'll be as fat as a pig,' she laughed after she had been there a week and had agreed, after much urging, to stay on a little longer. She had just got up from the tea table and was helping her aunt to clear the dishes away. 'My flat-mate won't recognise me when I get back to London.'

'And a good thing too,' the older woman smiled. 'You looked as if you were wasting away when you arrived. I don't know what you young girls get up to living on your own. You don't look after yourselves properly. You'll learn when you've a man of your own to care for.'

Kate winced. Although she had tried to put Nicholas firmly out of her thoughts he refused to stay buried. Every waking moment there was something to remind her of him, especially here where she had first met him. She supposed the pain would fade in time. She certainly hoped so. At the moment it was a dull ache which never left her. As she carried the dishes into the kitchen and plunged them into a bowl of soapy water she wondered what he was doing now. Probably still at the office, she decided, and caught herself worrying about the workload and how he would manage without her. Well, that was his problem, she told herself firmly, and tried to ignore it.

The doorbell rang just as she was finishing the last of the washing-up. 'I'll go,' she called to Aunt Meg, who, on her instructions, was taking a well-earned rest and watching her favourite television programme. She opened the door, the soapy water still dripping from her hands, and then reeled back in amazement at the sight of the figure on the doorstep.

'Nicholas?' she asked, hardly able to believe her eyes. 'What are you doing here?'

He ignored the question. 'May I come in?' he said. 'The doorstep's no place for a conversation.'

'Yes, of course.' She let him in and shut the door, then led the way into the dining room.

'Who was it, dear?' Aunt Meg appeared in the doorway and stopped short at the sight of their visitor. 'Why, it's Mr Blake, isn't it?'

'You have a good memory for names,' he complimented her, his smile charming her as it had done before. 'I wanted to speak to your niece. Her flat-mate told me she was here, so I drove down from London.'

'Yes, of course.' Aunt Meg ignored Kate's beseeching glance and announced that she would leave them. 'I'll be in the other room if you want me,' she said, and left tactfully.

Kate's eyes devoured the sight of him hungrily. Was it just her imagination playing tricks or did he look rather drawn and tired? She supposed the drive down here on top of a heavy day's work was enough to tire anyone. But he was not dressed in his working clothes. Instead he wore casual dark slacks and a cream polo-necked jersey which clung to him and emphasised every muscle of his broad frame. She felt her senses weakening as she looked at him and pulled herself up sharply.

'Would you like some coffee? You look as if you need some,' she asked him hastily before he had a chance to speak.

'Later, perhaps,' he said. His glance had not left her since she had opened the door to him. 'We have something to discuss first.'

'I'm not coming back to work for you,' she told him nervously. 'You may be having trouble replacing me and I'm sorry about that, but——'

'Who says I'm asking you back?' he said. He was cool and confident as he stood there and she envied him his composure. But then presumably she did not have the effect on him that his presence was having on her.

'Is everything all right at the office, then?' she asked.

'Yes. I've found a replacement for your job. She's rather slow and she jumps every time I come into the room, but I have high hopes of training her into something eventually.'

'Oh, I see.' Kate's face fell. She supposed she had been

hoping that he might at least say that he had missed her talents in the office. Now it seemed that she was instantly replaceable. She gave a brave smile which wavered slightly as she told him, 'You see, I was right, you can cope with everything, can't you?'

'Almost everything.' He moved towards her and took her in his arms, his hands firm but gentle against her. 'I've come to offer you a new job, if you'll take it on, Kate. Although I'll warn you now that it's quite a taxing one.'

'Oh?' She was as tense as a coiled spring, unable to relax, worried about what he would say next.

His eyes scanned her face as if trying to take in every detail. Then he said irrelevantly, 'I had trouble getting out of your flat-mate exactly where you were.'

'Did you?' She was even more bewildered now.

'She tried to give me a piece of her mind. Fortunately I was able to calm her down in the end and find out what I was supposed to have done.'

She was silent. Jane must have told him. How could she? She could not bear him to know of her love and either pity or laugh at her.

His hand beneath her chin forced her head up to meet his gaze. 'She told me about you and Jeremy Edwards, Kate. All of it. And she also told me that you were in love with me, not him. Is it true?'

There was no point in lying to him. Besides, she was not sure if she was capable of doing so. 'Yes,' she said.

She thought at first she imagined the light that blazed in his eyes as she abandoned herself to his kiss. But when, ages later, she came back to reality, she hardly recognised the warmth in his face, transforming it to a tenderness that she had never seen before. 'But what about the job?' she asked in dazed fashion.

He drew her closer to him, smiling. 'I'm not in the market for a personal assistant any more. I want a wife.

Do you think you would fit the bill?'

'What?'

He continued, making every word sound like an endearment, 'You're impossible, Kate. You make me lose my control faster than any woman I've ever met, you tempt me, you drive all thoughts of work out of my head. You even disturb my dreams. For God's sake, put me out of my misery and marry me!'

'*You* lose sleep over *me*?' She sounded incredulous.

'Too much. It's not good for my temper, as my new secretary can no doubt tell you,' he said. 'Kate? *Will* you marry me?' For the first time since she had known him she saw doubt in his face, uncertainty as to her answer. 'I know I've hurt you badly, but I'll make it up to you, I promise. I love you so much. I was nearly out of my mind with jealousy when you said you were determined to see Edwards again. You were right to be angry with me. I thought I could manage without you, but I never want to go through a week like the last one without you, as long as I live. Kate? Say something!'

Her face gave him his answer.

'Oh, Kate!' he groaned. He kissed her again, moulding her close to him, making her aware of how much he needed her. 'When will you marry me?'

'Is tomorrow too soon?' she asked.

'I'll see what I can do.' He bent his head to kiss her again and it was some time before he released her, flushed and radiant and in no doubt of his feeling for her.

'Nicholas,' she said hesitantly, but knowing the question had to be asked. 'What about Diana?'

'Nothing about Diana,' he replied steadily. 'She's gone. In fact I hear she has her eye on someone she's met in the Bahamas. I understand he owns two dozen oil wells.'

'But——'

'I know. She was on the way out when you came into

my life. I retained her at first out of sheer self-defence. You were all I'd ever hoped for, yet I was scared. I didn't want to fall for you. But I couldn't help myself. Later when you appeared to be involved with Edwards and told me to stop interfering I suppose I was trying to prove to myself and you that I could always find plenty of other women. But it was no use, you were the only one I really needed, and I suppose deep down I knew it from the first time I kissed you.'

'You called me an overgrown schoolgirl,' she told him indignantly. 'After we're married you can make up for being so insulting.'

'I fully intend to, my darling. And I'll start now.'

And when Aunt Meg poked her head round the door to ask if Mr Blake had everything he needed she rightly concluded that he had, and smiled as she went away again.